RUINED BY EXCESS
PERFECTED BY LACK
THE PARADOX OF PET NUTRITION

Richard S. Patton PhD

Ruined By Excess, Perfected By Lack
The Paradox Of Pet Nutrition
Richard S. Patton PhD

Dogs Naturally Publishing
A Division of Dogs Naturally Magazine Inc
PO Box 694, Beeton, Ontario, Canada L0G1A0
1-877-665-1290
www.dogsnaturallymagazine.com
info@dogsnaturallymagazine.com

Disclaimer
This information in this book is true and complete to the best of our knowledge and is meant to help pet owners find better nutritional options for their animals. It is not meant to replace veterinary advice or care. The author and publisher disclaim any liability in connection with the use of this information.

DEDICATION

The time and place of one's birth, and the accompanying DNA, are entirely the mischief of others. Regarding these others, I had all the good luck one could need for an entire life, just by virtue of who I was to call mother and father.

To my parents

Stu and Colleen Patton

ACKNOWLEDGMENTS

As books go, this one is not large, but it was the major preoccupation of my after hours life for over a decade. The ambition to undertake this task was enabled by the confidence shown in me by various superiors in my professional career. Paul Chandler, Mark Morris, Meyer Luskin and Hassan Kassem were quite simply my professional mentors. It is my hope this book in some small way validates the judgment and patience of these men.

Despite years of formal education and training, just about everything I know of any real application to the care of animals was taught to me by animals and their owners.

Beyond dedication or acknowledgement: It goes without saying that absent the loyalty and tireless devotion of my wife Elayne, this book, indeed my career, would not exist. That I want a matter of record.

TABLE OF CONTENTS

RICHARD S. PATTON PHD

In over 40 years as an animal nutritionist, Dr. Patton has worked in 25 countries and formulated diets for nearly every kind of animal. His formal study was at Penn State, Purdue and Virginia Tech. He was marketing manager for a company that recycled human food waste to animal feeds and Director of Research for Prescription Diet pet foods. As a consultant based in New Mexico for the past 30 years, Patton has worked for agriculture enterprises, zoos, foreign governments, Fortune 500 companies, local and regional feed mills and pet food companies. An adjunct professor at Penn State for 15 years, he has 25 scientific publications, two patents, a prior edition of this book (pet nutrition) and numerous popular press articles. Some of his past research efforts have focused on Vitamin E, chelated minerals and energy metabolism of the birthing mother. Patton's role in the market place is to serve as a translator of technical insight for the benefit of the animal and the animal owner. (www.pattonanimalnutrition.com)

1

INTRODUCTION

A hearty appetite for adventure and the winds of fate have allowed me to go to a variety of places, geographically and philosophically, where few if any in the world have been. My experience and years of travel afford me a viewpoint that is unique, and I share it with you in this book. Trained as a scientist, I have worked for decades around the world as an animal nutritionist. Because of all the different animals in the world for which I have formulated diets, I think it fair to call myself a comparative nutritionist, and I feel qualified to comment on the nutrition of animals, especially as it pertains to fundamentals and basic concepts. For example, identified in this book is a cause of obesity yet to be considered in full by the veterinary profession or the pet food industry. This concept, that excess soluble carbohydrate can be a dietary problem, is now being discussed in the human scientific literature, but it took over 20 years from its first mention in the technical journals to reach its present modest level of discussion.

If one would instruct, it is vital that the student see relevance in what they are asked to learn. This book attempts to provide such relevance by using the perspective of three fundamentals. The first is the nutrient makeup of the primordial world. Pure logic dictates that nothing could evolve to require a nutrient not present in its environment, and alternatively, to require a nutrient absent in the environment meant automatic extinction. However, the nutrition offered by the primordial world was variable in quality, nutrient density, abundance, time and place.

The second fundamental is the exquisite dietary adaptability of mammals; it explains an animal's survival when the environment offers a temporary lack of a needed nutrient. As we shall see, animals have an almost endless ability to deal with lack, if allowed to behave as nature intended. This is the third fundamental, that innate behavior must be afforded an animal to allow it to adapt to this variable diet.

The major ambition of this book is to explain why, despite this exquisite adaptability, a modern animal can still be malnourished. Sometimes, with the best of intentions, in our ignorance we force behavior changes on our animals, and these changes can be crucial to nutrition. An even more pervasive problem is that our evolution, and that of our animal friends, was an exquisite perfection of dealing with lack of nutrients, in particular, energy. Because there never was any real drive to adapt to an excess of energy, there is poor adaptability to modern diets if they are too high in certain types of calories. This is a variation of the "thrifty gene" concept invoked in the discussion of primordial societies intersecting with modern technology. What is detailed in this book is an explanation of why, despite a domesticated animal's adaptability, its probable fate is to be malnourished unless people apply the fundamentals of nutrition.

Besides formal training and professional experience, I have for 30 years indulged a passion that afforded me another vantage point in understanding diet and nutrition. Each year I would disappear into the wilderness of the Rocky Mountains, traveling by horse and emulating in exact detail the explorers of the early nineteenth century. There is precedent for this concept of field laboratory reconstruction in the annals of anthropology. In the 1940s, Thor Heyerdahl and his colleagues navigated a primitive raft across the Pacific from Peru to the nearest inhabited island, a distance of over 4,000 miles. Their aim was to prove, that with the aid of trade winds and currents, prehistoric man could accomplish such a voyage. The adventure was recounted in the popular book *Kon Tiki* (1950, Rand McNally, New York, NY), wherein Heyerdahl told of numerous anthropologic insights, none of which would have been encountered by office bound scholars.

In our field laboratory, we lived off the land, fending for ourselves with 1830s equipment. This meant no waterproofing or matches, and otherwise only primitive tools of that time period. While we thought it high adventure and great fun, we were often 50 miles from any civilization and in fact not playing at all but surviving in the wilderness with Lewis and Clark technology. As we perfected this pursuit over the years, and trained as I was to observe and collect data, I gathered insight regarding the behavior of man and beast in a natural setting and the effect of nutrition obtained from the surroundings in an ancient and primeval way.

There are numerous useful books on modern nutrition, at least a half dozen on the primordial diet of our ancestors, and several dozen on companion animal nutrition. For yourself, you know for the most part what to eat and what not to eat, and everyone knows to get regular exercise and apply portion control at meals. Despite all these books and accumulated insight, there is still something lacking in our approach to our own nutrition and the nutrition of the animals in our care. For one thing, 40 percent of our pets are overweight (*Business Week*, August 6, 2007). Veterinary medicine is like other biomedical fields, flooded with new technology, leaving little time for a preventative approach. Thus, it becomes crisis oriented. Not too often is nutrition a crisis; it slowly gets worse and worse until something else is a crisis.

Figure 1 *Veterinary medicine is crisis oriented. Nutrition is rarely a crisis.*

The study of nutrition is circuitous in nature. It does not have an obvious starting point. Should one first discuss the composition of food, its protein or fat? Do you begin with the purpose and function of each food component, or start first with the many factors that alter nutrient requirements? Any one aspect of a topic is interrelated to many others, and can't be understood as a standalone discussion. (Figure 2).

Figure 2 *The study of nutrition requires an understanding of many disciplines.*

For example, as we'll see, a discussion about protein is incomplete without a consideration of energy. Zinc needs are not static, but influenced by stress. The total calories consumed are only part of the story. The source of the calories or type (from fat or carbohydrate or protein) is more important than the total consumed. Fat as a nutrient has over twice the caloric content of sugar, but as we'll see, compared to sugar, it is innocent in the cause of obesity. Believe it or not, this has been known and ignored for more than 100 years. Different species use varied strategies to achieve nourishment from the environment. Herbivores harvest large quantities of plants, while carnivores harvest small quantities of herbivores. Some creatures can eat almost anything, and under duress often do, but there is clear specialization, making generalizations across all species hard to apply unless looking at the cellular level.

With nutrition such a fascinating collision of so many disciplines, it is only fair to announce to you ahead of time what map we will follow in discussing the different aspects of nutrition science. First off, you deserve to know the major details of my journey that in my opinion qualify me as experienced in animal nutrition. I have spent an entire career as a student of animal nutrition, thus a few pages are devoted to telling you about me. The story begins in earnest in Chapter 2 with a review of the major components of food, with the aim of outlining the foundation rules of nutrition, the language used and its meaning. What is meant by the word protein? Or carbohydrate? What is a calorie, really? Any discussion requires an agreement on what words mean. Chapter 2 is the most cumbersome, or some may say driest, with a necessary look at the organic makeup of food. Every effort was made to keep the dialogue in Chapter 2 light and simplistic (the dullest stuff was banished to the end notes), but still it will require your patience and forbearance.

With nomenclature defined, in Chapter 3 we then go back and look at where we came from, what was food not only for our ancestors, but for early hominids, the dinosaurs and even before them. Chapter 4 is a look at the beautiful yet little mentioned genius of mammalian survival, adaptability, and in particular one modern day challenge for adaptability. Chapter 5 is another boot camp sort of topic, anatomy and digestive physiology, but I can't have you going away thinking the cow and the horse are the same or the tiger and the house cat are different. Species take different routes getting down to the molecular level of nutrition, but once there, all life forms are nearly identical.

In Chapter 6, the non-nutritional topic of behavior is considered for its very significant impact on nutrition. I quite enjoyed putting together Chapters 7 through 12, but I am not so naïve as to think everyone eagerly waits to devour pointy-head speak. Cat owners and horse owners get their own chapter, but the blow by blow on microbe supplements, vitamin, minerals, and especially the one on laws and regulations, are not easy to make entertaining. These chapters might just as well be viewed as reference material, and read more generally.

But in the final chapter 13 we are again full on. Read it more carefully. It's the wrap on the entire saga.

Even though this is a book about the nutrition of animals, I often talk about human nutrition. I feel this helps in several ways. Most people are familiar with their own nutrition (they do eat three times a day) and can relate in an intimate way to such a discussion. The field of human nutrition is quite advanced compared to any one animal, and most of what is known about humans (animals themselves don't forget) can be applied to animals. Much of the knowledge about human nutrition was first resolved using animal models. Regarding nutrition, there is far more in common between a dog and a man than not, and at the cellular level, there is no appreciable difference.

Animal nutrition problems, on close analysis, are often people problems. If for no other reason, this is true because by confinement we deny our companion animals (indeed all domesticated animals) their innate behavior, which has kept them vital and fit since the beginning of time. Of course we can't release from confinement all confined creatures. Marauding grizzly bears in downtown Manhattan would not work very well. There are no easy solutions, only intelligent alternatives. My ambition with this book is not to tell you what to do, but rather to provide insight and information for your decision-making process.

ANIMAL NUTRITION. THE PATH THAT CHOSE ME.

It was heartbreaking to watch the mother cat try to walk among her kittens. Her balance would fail her and she'd fall on her side. It was early on in my career, and I realized I'd probably never grow indifferent to animal suffering. I had a position where it was my responsibility to arrange the mating of the cats so that we had a steady flow of kittens. This was because our function as an organization was to provide an Underwriters Laboratories type service for the pet food industry. Companies would hire our facility to prove their diets did as they claimed, for example, maintain adults or grow puppies. It was my job to oversee these tests and ensure that our conclusion was unbiased and scientifically correct.

A constant availability of litters of dogs and cats was thus necessary to verify the nutritional adequacy of different diets that our clients wished to market. Of all our female cats (called queens), this one was my favorite. She was a big grey lady, with striking yellow eyes, and she was so sweet and friendly. With a cattery of over 200 individuals, there was not time to tame and gentle each cat, so the ones so disposed were easy to appreciate.

For mating, toms and queens were rotated through a sequence that specifically avoided inbreeding, and I looked forward to the time when the rotation would pair my favorite queen with my favorite tom. This fellow was also very approachable and kind. He was large, and all male, with a thick neck, and he invariably sired large healthy litters. He was black and white, quite like a Holstein cow. From the mating of these two fine feline specimens, there were six kittens in the litter, four black, one grey like the mother, and one Holstein, like the sire. Their mother was superb at her job. On her milk, these kittens gained weight at the proscribed rate and looked great. But three weeks after birth, she got an ear infection, which affected her balance and caused obvious discomfort. Of course, we had vets on staff and she had the best of medical care, and she continued to care for her kittens and try to nurse them, but her milk nearly dried up and the kittens stopped gaining weight.

The infection was cleared up in a week or so, and soon it was time to wean the kittens, which by protocol was six weeks of age. I found I had a dilemma on my hands. The kittens were barely half the weight we expected at weaning, which disqualified them for any test measuring the ability of a diet to support growth. Should I leave them with their mother, whose milk flow seemed to have revived, or wean them per protocol and hope for the best? This was my first real professional job, and I was conflicted, afraid of being seen as too compassionate, and afraid of mistreating the kittens. At any rate, I directed that they be weaned on time at six weeks of age, and followed what ensued with anxious concern.

There is a very predictable growth curve following weaning, which always starts out with a sharp decline in growth as the kittens deal with the stress of weaning, the most traumatic thing to happen to them in their young lives. Much to my amazement, my prize litter of kittens never even noticed weaning. When removed from their mother and placed on dry food (the same one their mother had been eating) they gained weight at an accelerating rate, never showing any lessening of gain or evidence of stress. In three weeks (at nine weeks of age) they were in fact ahead of the standard curve for growth rate.

The person in charge of the day to day care of our cats was one of those serendipitous placements encountered on occasion in a work force. He was a born natural at cat care, and even he did not suspect this when hired. For him, there was no timid or unapproachable cat in the entire facility, despite the fact that for the rest of us, almost every cat was impossible to corral, even with a net.

When discussing my amazement at the litter's performance, he did not at all share my bewilderment. "Oh, they were weaned at three weeks," he told me, "back when their mother got sick." When her milk diminished and they got hungry, they learned right away to eat her food. I went back and looked at the food consumption records routinely collected on all our animals. There it was in black and white. The mother's food consumption appeared to increase when she got sick, but of course it was her kittens eating the food, not her. When we weaned the kittens at six weeks of age, they had already been weaned, and as I thought about it, in a far less stressful way than normal. They had the care and nurturing of their mother as they went through the stress of weaning.

This experience had a profound effect on me. First of all, as my father taught me early on, you never know for certain when you're winning or when you're losing. What seems at the time like the worst possible development may prove the best thing that could have happened to you. Conversely, a great day may soon prove a wrong turn in your life. The other lesson the kittens brought into very clear focus for me was animals' near miraculous adaptability to harsh or cruel conditions. This is a theme we'll encounter in detail in later chapters. Most important, this episode with my favorite mother cat and her kittens was the beginning of a career-long truth for me. Despite a lot of formal education, nearly everything I learned about animal nutrition I was taught by animals and their owners.

The day I discovered animal nutrition is vivid in my mind. I was 19 and attending college in the hopes that something would present itself that interested me. I did not doubt that college was a worthwhile place to be, but the pre-med curriculum track I was on loomed as a formidable task given my type of intellect, and in those days, one was assured of prompt induction in the army if not in college. I had switched out of pre-med, and the C minus grade average I was accumulating, to general arts and science. To my frustration, the C minus followed me into arts and science. I always had a big soft spot for animals, so I took a course in animal nutrition taught by Dr. Paul Hartsook of the Penn State Department of Animal Science. The classroom was right next to the Armsby calorimeter where, over 100 years ago, Dr. Armsby's pioneering research in energy metabolism unfolded, and to this day is the basis of much of what is understood in the field. Little did I suspect that I would one day study energy metabolism to the furthest edge of the known science.

In the mid-60s, nutrition was looked down upon by all the hard sciences. The nutrition department was often part of the home economics group and considered the realm of Betty Crocker and future homemakers. But Dr. Hartsook revealed the science in a logical way and I saw genuine relevance to the subject matter, which was a sentiment that had escaped me in other courses. It can't be said that one day in an abrupt redirect I took animal nutrition as my path, born again as they say, but I did change my major field of study to animal science. Regarding the grade point average, the Cs I had struggled to accomplish now were As and Bs and happened almost without trying. I even managed to make dean's list, despite numerous courses in biochemistry and statistics. I concluded, as most educators know, that grade point average for college students is just as much a measure of motivation and maturity as intellect.

As I look back on the day, I sometimes feel there was an inner wisdom operating. I saw the study of animal nutrition as a chance to be a scientist and a cowboy at the same time. Upon reflection, this would not be an inaccurate overview of my career to date. It has been my privilege to work all over the world, most often in boots and jeans with the occasional coat and tie, helping animals by helping their owners apply the most recent insights of nutrition science.

College was followed by graduate school at Purdue, where I specialized in the effect of nutrition on reproduction, and earned a master's degree, then Virginia Tech for a Ph.D., where the course work in biochemistry and statistics continued. At Virginia Tech I researched the feeding of insects to cows. This was driven by my premonition that the exoskeleton of insects, containing chitin, could be digested by the bacteria in the cow's rumen (paunch). It proved to be so. My thinking, dismissed with a patronizing smile by most of my colleagues, was that insects represented an over-looked reservoir of quality nutrition. Society spends billions to eradicate insects because they eat or destroy one third of all food produced in the world. In indus-trialized countries, if people are aware of insect costs, it is in the form of insecti-cides used in agriculture, or the friendly exterminator. People in poor economies, or those living in the tropics, encounter insect damage on a more regular basis. At any rate, I was proposing, with this demonstration of the utility of insects as feed for cows, that society consider spending a few million dollars to harvest insects rather than billions to eradicate them. I thought cow manure would be a warm feast for a cockroach, and the symmetry of this recycling (cow waste feeds insects that are fed to cows) seemed full of potential.

This thinking was evidently too irrelevant for the time, and the research when pub-lished landed with a dull thud. As I recall, there were three requests for a reprint of the article from within the United States. There were more than 50 from elsewhere in the world. I concluded that not everyone saw the idea as irrelevant, but people's viewpoints were quite influenced by what country they called home. My ambition to help feed the world, and if at all possible recycle while doing it, was a lasting legacy of my graduate work.

I left graduate school without a job. It was 1972 and there was a sizeable economic downturn in the offing. Consequently, I took a job as a cowboy near Reno, Nevada. I bought a truck and loaded the family in it and we headed west, not unlike a scene from The Grapes of Wrath. I had worked on ranches in Nevada during college and the ethos of the state quite appealed to me, not to mention the high desert beauty. Within six months, a real job presented itself and I flew off to Kansas for an in-terview. I remember they asked me what sort of salary I had in mind and I replied, with all honesty, that whatever they could get someone else to do the job for, I'd do it for less. So I started my professional life in the big world making $13,000 a year.

This first professional employment following my formal education was with the animal nutrition research lab discussed at the beginning of this chapter. The facility was founded by the Mark Morris family to continue the pioneering efforts of Dr. Mark Morris, Sr. in the dietary management of disease in companion animals. Dr.

8

Morris was the first to propose a low quantity, high quality protein diet for kidney failure in dogs. Prescription Diet k/d, as it was called, was the flagship product in a line of such diets that afforded veterinarians and their clients a useful dietary tool to help with specific afflictions in pets.

My assignment at first was to oversee the research trials, and subsequently in the front office as an assistant in professional education. This meant I drafted literature for veterinarians on the dietary management of disease. My qualifications for this were due to the wide experience I gained under the direction of the late Mark Morris, Jr., son of the founder. Dr. Morris (Jr.) felt it was better if a DVM communicated with other DVMs, so as a Ph.D. I was precluded from a starring role in some of the effort but I was given wide discretion in zoo animal nutrition research. Here I enjoyed myself and had many rare experiences for an animal nutritionist. In the chapters that follow, reference is made often to my experience with exotic animals to illustrate principles common to all animals. A diligent employee could look forward to an entire career working for the Morris family, but spending the rest of my life in Kansas was unthinkable. I grew restless.

A job opening in Los Angeles was brought to my attention. It was as a marketing manager for a company that recycled day old bread into animal food. This company had five plants around the country. They saw their options as two: hire a business oriented individual and teach him nutrition, or hire a nutritionist and hope he could learn business. I was successful in talking them into giving me a try, and I spent the next four years in Los Angeles, trying in earnest to prove they had not made a mistake. Again, I was lucky that the owner of the company, Meyer Luskin, was willing to be patient with me while I learned the ins and outs of business, and tried my best to be a corporate animal.

To this point in my career, the only training I had was as a scientist, and my only experience as a cowboy and animal nutritionist. I usually had to learn important lessons the hard way, but at least I became conversant with concepts like accounts receivable and accounts payable. A Ph.D. in science is not very often afforded the opportunity to gather business acumen, and I must say, those four years in Los Angeles were tantamount to an MBA for me. Ever since, my clients and I have benefited from this broadening of my perspective. *End Notes page 160.*

To say "day old bread" was an oversimplification. Route trucks retrieved dumpsters full of raw material from food companies all over the city and southern California and other major cities. This raw material could be day old bread, unsold in the stores and sent back to the bakery. But there was also pasta, crackers, snack foods, flour, donuts and pastries. In short, almost any human food that would process in our plant's system was used. This involved a series of specially developed machinery that mixed and dried the raw material while also removing all traces of packaging such as paper, plastic and cellophane. Magnets throughout the facility removed all metal from the feed. The end product was a dry grain-like feed that mirrored the diet of people in the region; it was high in fat, salt and soluble carbohydrate. What this said about the human diet we will consider in some detail later. From my perspective, I was helping to feed the world and recycling. This product was offered to the animal feed industry at a more attractive price than competing grains. Useful human food was rescued, owners fed their animals a little more economically and the company made some profit. Everybody won, including me, who had a job.

It soon became evident I was a poor fit in this job. Living in the city exacted a toll I was reluctant to pay, and worse, my success on any given day was measured by how much dried bakery product got sold. This was only fair, for such is the nature of business. While I struggled to be an adequate salesman, I did learn something I much needed to see: if you got it, a salesman sold it. The salesman made the United States what it is, an economic powerhouse never before seen in the history of the world. In business, either you are a salesman, or directly supporting a salesman, or you are superfluous. As I have lectured to audiences around the world, little else I say meets more resistance than this opinion of mine about salesmen. But this resistance comes from employees who are neither salesmen nor directly in their support, usually middle management, and I will stand by my viewpoint on this.

For my part, one of the biggest lessons I learned in my tenure in city corporate life was that I am not a good salesman. But this cleared the way for a more useful and realistic understanding: a salesman with me at his side will sell even more. My career in technical transfer was ready to take form. This happened in 1980, when I left Los Angeles and joined my former graduate school advisor in a consulting business.

As my major professor in graduate school at Virginia Tech, Dr. Paul Chandler had been another of those long-suffering superiors that watched me fumble towards adult behavior. He had been a graduate student in my father's department when I was in college at Penn State and invited me to be his graduate student when he left for a faculty position at Virginia Tech. As I related, I went off instead to get a master's degree at Purdue, but within a year had called Chandler to ask if his offer still held. He said, "You come on," so my last two years of formal education (1970 - 1972) were under his guidance. In 1980, we came together again in a consulting partnership.

Since then, I have been an independent animal nutrition consultant. I have heard it said that consulting is what you do if you can't find a job. I have been a consultant for a long time, and managed to get the bills paid all along, so maybe this observation doesn't pertain to everyone. I do know now that I am pretty much unemployable in the traditional sense. It would appear that I have an attitude that blends poorly in the corporate world. I have always had a near pathological problem with authority, and one person controlling my fate somehow brought out an independent streak in me. I came to see myself as an outside dog, living under the porch. Sometimes, on frigid nights, the outside dog peers through the window at the inside dog next to the fireplace, and he thinks how nice life would be as an inside dog. But then he remembers he doesn't have to ask anyone to go outside to pee, and he gets back under the porch and somehow makes it through the night.

I know there is some degree of outside dog in everyone, but for some, like myself, independence is just too precious, and I have forsaken a high salary and perks to live where I wanted and do as I pleased. Of course, this is all a frame of mind, more than anything else, as in reality I worked far more hours, lived on an airplane or in a hotel and was never beyond the reach of my clients. For me, the important part was I could have a day off whenever I wanted. The fact that I almost never took a day off was my choice.

My client list has always been diverse. Among my clients have been zoos and companies that make food for zoos, dairy farmers, ranchers, horse farms, pet food companies, feed mills, companies that made special ingredients, recycling companies, foreign governments and international development firms. Among all my clients, the common denominator was animal nutrition. This work has taken me to more than 25 foreign countries, and the insights and adventures have been priceless. Always, the only colors I flew were those of an animal nutritionist who recommended in the best interest of the animal and the animal's owner. And this was my policy regardless of who was paying me. If a company hired me to explain the nutritional biochemistry of their product to prospective customers, and because of the circumstances at hand I did not think it was in the customer's best interest to buy, I said so, with my paying client standing right there. On the rare occasion this happened, and a sale was lost for the moment, the candor won respect for my client, which most often proved a larger victory in due time.

Because I felt many animal nutrition problems were human in origin, and it risked my job security to say it that way, I developed a method of questioning my clients and their employees that helped us get at the root cause of problems. I asked the same question repeatedly using different words.

The need for persistent questioning became evident to me when we were test marketing a new diet for raptors (birds of prey) in zoos. I was of the growing suspicion that mother eagles regurgitated their food for the young, and in so doing, added enzymes that aided the chicks in digestion. The curator of birds at one of our test zoos was gifted with great powers of observation, and raptors were a deep professional interest of his. I felt lucky to have such a cooperator on the project. I asked him if he had ever seen the mother eagle regurgitate her food for the chicks. He replied "No, never; only seven times." With this, I had the answer I wanted, which was an accurate counting of how often it was observed. But what amazed me was that this very important behavior by the eagle mother was inconsequential in the mind of the curator, and so to him his records of it were irrelevant. The curator was way above average at looking and really seeing what he was looking at. I was struck by the thought that if I had been dealing with a person of normal powers of observation, the answer would have been merely, "No, never." An opportunity to further my hypothesis would have been lost.

Recently, I was explaining a theory of mine (that constant excess soluble carbohydrate is not good) to another animal nutritionist. She politely endured my pontification, then asked how I explained her cat that died at 19 and ate dry food its entire life. (Dry food of the conventional expanded type so common in the market must be 30 to 50 percent soluble carbohydrate. Not good for a carnivore, in my opinion.) I admitted, recovering as best I could, that this was unique and probably made possible by the fact that the cat had adapted to self feeding at will. A few minutes later, as I stood by, she admonished another to reduce the weight of their cat, lest they have to give insulin shots twice a day for five years, as she did. I immediately confronted her, pointing out she withheld evidence of direct bearing to our discussion. Her cat was a brittle diabetic for the last five years of its life, supporting my theory, but she, an animal nutritionist, choose to dismiss the role of diet in her cat's affliction.

When first asked, people will tell you what they think you want to hear, then they'll tell you what they think you ought to hear. The third time you ask the question, you may hear from them what they think happened. And this is in a non-confrontational setting, which you are not always assured. Sometimes the employee caters to the boss or protects a fellow employee or incriminates another employee. I soon saw this as normal behavior done by us all. So after questioning everyone multiple times during the day, I always made sure I checked with another source: the animals. They always tell the truth and don't care who they tell it to. The frustration is that sometimes the information animals provide is in a riddle.

To illustrate this point, let me cite an experience I had. A client of mine had a cow or two a day that would weaken from some unknown malady and he would remove them from the main herd and put them in the sick pen. They mysteriously recovered in a few hours and were returned to the herd. Once back in the main herd, they soon were sick again. Returned to the sick pen once more, they recovered. It was not until the perplexed owner, almost by chance, put his hand into the water trough and got an electrical shock that the problem was solved. Bare electrical wires short-circuited the tank's heating system and gave a nasty shock to any animal trying to drink. The water tank in the sick pen was functioning properly, so after a drink there, the animals recovered, and were put back with the herd, only to go thirsty again. It has been my experience that all the clues you need, more often than not, are right before your eyes. The challenge is to see these clues and interrupt them in the right way.

Another crucial lesson I learned with untold embarrassment, perhaps the single most valuable insight I learned about consulting, is that people have very good reasons for doing things. They have arrived at their methods from years of experi-

sive trial and error. At the beginning of my career, I would see a situation I thought could be improved and just start reading my client the gospel according to Patton. With admirable patience, they would explain to their consultant why they did it that way, and I had to retreat, egg on my face. It didn't take too much of this for me to learn to ask questions and shut up and listen. I realized if I was going to recommend a change, my reasons for the change needed to be better than their reasons for their method in the first place. And how could I know their reasons if I didn't first ask them and listen to (and hear!) their answer?

2

MAJOR DIETARY COMPONENTS
(FOOD CHEMISTRY)

In addition to the major nutrient components of protein, fat, fiber, carbohydrate and minerals, there are two other nutrients of the highest significance. They are energy and water. Energy is not an ingredient that is added to the formula or assayed by the lab as a specific percent of the total, but we all know it is absolutely crucial. Its level in a diet is a direct function of what foods make up the diet or what ingredients are used. We'll take a close look at energy in a moment, but first water.

In most developed countries, water is taken for granted. One of the hallmark indicators, if not the single greatest indicator, of a progressive society is a safe and reliable water supply. Only a short time spent in an emerging economy and one soon appreciates the truth of this observation. One time in Egypt I watched as a man washed an entire Greyhound bus with one bucket of water. In the United States, the mere thought of doing this would be dismissed as absurd. But Egypt was also the place where I observed peasant women washing dishes in a canal that had a dead goat carcass floating only a few yards away. In America, safe water is everywhere. But it is not by accident or happenstance. It is due to generations of skilled engineers, dedicated public funding, rigorous laws and constant monitoring.

Although it is usually not discussed when talking nutrition, and it should need no mention, water is the first and most important nutrient. Only oxygen is more critical. All our animals need water on a regular basis. It is best if it is clean and fresh and of good quality. (We'll dispense with discussion about toxic or microbiologically unclean water. This alarming situation is very rare, thankfully, and quickly fixed.) Quality is compromised most often by mineral content. We have all experienced so-called hard water that corrodes faucets, tea kettles, ice trays and shower stalls. Hard water is not savory, but most creatures can extract what they need from hard water without undue harm. On a long term basis, it can be a problem, and if your water is hard, you probably avoid drinking it and buy good water at the grocery store for cooking and coffee. Do the same for your pets. Hard water problems in a pet usually first show up as poor hair coat. But then, just about every nutrition problem first shows up as poor coat.

Water can also be contaminated with other anti-metabolites, such as nitrates and high amounts of trace minerals, but your drinking water is invariably screened for these problems by the authorities who are prompt to correct them if found, so these are unlikely to persist. However, at least once a week, inspect your dog's water bowl. You will often notice it has a slippery film on it. This is the result of bacteria, and the bowl should be scrubbed with abrasive, soap and hot water to eliminate this film.

ENERGY

The discussion about energy has two parts. The amount released in the body to sustain the activities of life, and the amount taken in to restore or replace the expended energy. In simple terms, exertion and diet. Over the long term, balance between these two equates with trim physique, and imbalance leads to death or obesity. We need not belabor the obvious, that people and their pets are in an obesity epidemic. The average male American gains two pounds a year from the age of 25 to 50, with the result that he is 50 pounds overweight by the age of 50, which is what the headlines and all the diet books are about. But let's not lose perspective. Two pounds a year is 2.5 grams a day in weight gain. This is not very much weight gain—less than a stick of gum. For a great many, a remarkable and effective system for caloric balance is working perfectly, and for many others, nearly so. A half hour of brisk walking, or almost any exercise of your choice, burns 250 calories, and some modest self-discipline with portion control will easily subtract another 250 calories. This 500 calorie swing over the years will virtually assure a slim body for many people. A rethinking of the source of these calories, whether from soluble carbohydrate, fat or protein, makes it even easier, as we'll see. The surprise is the ideal diet promoted for years by policy authorities is incomplete, if not wrong, and it need not take years to reverse obesity.

The same effective regulation of energy economy operates in our pets, with at least equal or finer precision. Some fox hunters have taken to carrying a GPS (global positioning system) that accumulates distance traveled. At the end of a three-hour hunt, members of the field have sometimes ridden their horses 25 miles. The hounds have done at least twice that distance, or 50 miles in three hours. Endurance sled dogs travel up to 80 miles a day, burning over 11,000 calories. This is the equivalent on an equal weight basis of a man burning 38,000 calories in a day. These towering feats of exercise are atypical, but serve to illustrate a dog's inherent capacity for boundless energy. As commendable and beneficial as it is, when you walk 20 minutes, and your dog cavorting about the whole while, you haven't even begun to tap what is there. How a hound can run 50 miles in three hours twice a week and not lose body weight, while an apartment bound Airedale goes nowhere yet stays trim, cannot be explained fully by the amount eaten. Yes, Iditarod dogs do lose weight, and completely sedentary dogs can gain weight, but what is fascinating is the incredible span in caloric use rate and the flexibility and adaptation it represents. There must be internal switches and regulators we have yet to discover or understand. Cats, discussed in detail in Chapter 9, are even more interesting. Many domestic cats, as well as wild lions and tigers, sleep up to 18 hours a day.

Animals eat to meet their energy needs. In the natural state, when they have consumed enough calories, they stop eating. The same mechanism operates in people, but it is pretty well obliterated by our culture. The problem begins with the childhood admonition to clean up your plate, and continues throughout life in many other guises. For our pets, we bring our own confusion to the discussion, and combine it with the double talk inscribed on pet food labels. Pet food labels are not misleading on purpose, but one must be a nutritionist to decipher them, and, once this is done, it is realized that only partial information has been provided.

It is a fundamental rule of animal nutrition that the diet be balanced. What is meant by a balanced diet is all the other nutrients must be balanced to the energy content. When the animal has consumed the calories it needs, and stops eating, it must also have consumed the correct amount of all other essential nutrients. A diet very high in calories and low in protein would lead to a problem. When the animal had stopped eating because its caloric needs had been met, it would not have consumed enough protein. This is the source of the term tossed about in the popular press of "empty calories," meaning a food that is not balanced with the other essential nutrients.

Energy can be a confusing topic. First of all, as a concept, it is an abstraction that can only be measured when it changes from one form to another. It is quantified in units called calories, but as we'll see, the energy of a diet is not described just by the sum of the calories in the food. A calorie is the amount of energy required to raise the temperature of one cubic centimeter or cc (which is also by definition a gram)of water from 16.5 to 17.5 degrees centigrade. If you would envision a syringe the thickness of a pencil, a cc is about a half inch of this syringe. A calorie represents a very small number so most discussions are in fact about kilocalories, which is to say 1000 calories, abbreviated kcal. All the talk about our daily caloric intake, or calories for exercise, is really about kcal, even though the term used is invariably calories.

ENERGY DISCUSSION:
THE FIRST HALF, REQUIREMENTS (OR WHAT IS NEEDED BY THE BODY).

It is possible to estimate with fair accuracy how many calories a warm blooded animal needs for basal metabolic rate (BMR). Basal metabolic rate would be one's energy requirements just before getting out of bed after a night of sleep, the lowest in the 24 hour day. *End Notes page 160.*

Upon arising and going about the day, basal metabolic rate gives rise to metabolic rate. This varies a lot from one individual to the next. One reason is the wide range in metabolic efficiency among individuals. We all know those who eat whatever they want and seem to stay thin, while others have to always apply portion control and restraint yet still fight the battle of the bulge.

This fact I have observed repeatedly in different animal species. We designed a diet of specific caloric density such that 250 grams a day would maintain a 40 pound beagle at constant weight under controlled activity. We found some 40 pound beagles needed 300 grams and others only 200.

We once did a nitrogen balance study with horses for a drug company. The first step in such research is to feed each individual horse so that the nitrogen excreted in the urine and feces equals (balances) the nitrogen consumed. All horses were fed a commercial diet advertised as complete and balanced for adult horse maintenance. To achieve nitrogen balance in the 40 horses in the trial, all carefully controlled for activity, 18 required the addition of some amount of corn, an energy feed, and 18 required the addition of some amount of soybean meal, a protein feed. Only four, or 10 percent, of the 40 horses maintained on the diet without any supplementation.

A refined look at the variation in metabolic efficiency can be seen in the dairy cow when monitored each day for milk production as well as body weight. Eating the same amounts of the same ration, cows can vary over 20 percent in their efficiency of converting feed into milk. Poultry, both for eggs and meat, beef and swine are all carefully evaluated for feed conversion, this number being the single largest factor in their owner's profitability. A variation of 20 percent in feed conversion efficiency is routine, and this stems directly from variability in metabolic efficiency.

So despite the fact that the equation for basal metabolic rate has stood the test of time as well as just about any biomedical insight, we still are reduced to the trained eye of the keeper for getting caloric intake correct. Individual variation in metabolic efficiency is too broad to allow any useful generalization. More about this later when we discuss labels on pet food packaging.

ENERGY DISCUSSION: THE SECOND HALF, WHAT'S IN THE DIET

The caloric content of a food or diet is usually described in one of three different ways, none of which are the whole story or correct to use in all cases. These three ways to list the caloric content of a diet are gross energy, digestible energy or metabolizable energy. Pet food labels always talk in terms of metabolizable energy. *End Notes page 161.*

An example of how to determine calories in a pet food is shown in the Appendix, page 169. It is recognized that this process is less than straightforward, and it is best to leave the task to a nutritionist. It is not that the concepts or the math are difficult. It's because the information on the package is incomplete and requires assumptions that are generally safe. Furthermore, once the total calories are calculated, to be truly accurate the value needs to be determined by actual feeding trials in animals. This is very expensive and rarely done. More often, it is estimated or extrapolated from similar diets. Such extrapolation can be wide of the actual truth. The same ingredient is not digested and absorbed the same way every time. For example, dried bakery product and dried distiller's grains are two byproducts occasionally used in pet food. If heated too much during their processing, which does happen on occasion, the digestibility of all their components declines, sometimes significantly. Very high quality pet foods can justify using 4, 4 and 9 for the gross caloric potency of protein, carbohydrate and fat, respectively. These pet foods are expensive. More honest values for some pet foods are 3.8, 3.8 and 8.5, to reflect the over-processed nature or lower quality of the ingredients. But as you can appreciate, these small adjustments are of little impact compared to changing the amount fed.

For most of us, a discussion about calories in a diet is often really about whether or not the diet will make an individual gain weight or become fat. While this is an oversimplification, let's consider this approach for a moment. There are factors besides diet energy content that influence obesity. Dietary energy density alone is not the problem or the solution to the problem. The observation that the best diet is exercise is catchy and well intentioned, but misleading.

Critical factors in the equation are age of the animal, the inherent metabolic rate and efficiency of the animal, the calories in the diet, the interaction of different components of the diet, the amount of diet eaten, the amount of exercise, the environmental temperature, and crucially, the source of the calories. By source I mean did the calories come from protein, carbohydrate or fat? As we'll see, the source of the calories has a big effect. If from carbohydrate, what kind? Was it fiber or starch, fructose or sucrose? With fat over twice the caloric content of carbohydrate, nutritionists for decades have been beguiled into assuming obesity was caused by too much fat. In fact, data has been available for decades that often obesity is caused by excess carbohydrates, not by eating too much or from lack of exercise.

It is easy to say about an obese pet that the solution is more exercise. To do so is to ignore the reality of many dogs and cats that live in apartments, or with inactive owners, or in such circumstances where exercise is not readily at hand. There are weight loss diets for dogs and cats sold all the time. Different strategies are employed, such as including more fiber. There is even a weight loss drug approved just recently for dogs. Regardless of which weight loss diet you buy, the pet is going to resist the caloric restriction and beg. It is just the same for people trying to lose weight. Despite what product promotion pushes at you, there is no completely convenient way to lose weight.

The most perfect plan still requires at least some measure of self-discipline. You will have to be resolved that weight loss is worth the temporary anxiety of your pet. One of the problems is that a fat dog or cat put on a diet that meets its daily needs for calories, and no more, will not get any fatter, but it will tend to stay fat if the diet composition is not changed. If the intent is to cause weight loss by feeding less of the diet that created obesity in the first place, it must be fed to provide less than the pet's daily needs for calories. It is the only way to send the body to its reserves and to start mobilizing the stored fat, the fat that was put in storage exactly for when energy intake was inadequate. So expect begging.

But take heart. The hard part is the first three days. After about three days on a diet, a metabolic shift takes place as depot fat (body reserves) is mobilized, the intestine's size begins to lessen, and the worst is over. Further, a diet designed to keep blood sugar at a constant level (in other words, a diet low in soluble carbohydrate) greatly assists in mobilizing body fat.

Begging probably will continue for a while, but that is a behavior problem, both on the part of the owner and the pet.

We can sum up the topic of energy with this: If all other factors are equal, the diet with the highest soluble carbohydrate will lead to obesity the soonest. However, all other factors are never equal, and we are left with the trained eye of the keeper as the best regulator of diet health. Four commercially available pet foods are listed in Table 1 below in abbreviated format (and in expanded format in the Appendix) showing their calculated energy levels. The range is not great, especially when you consider that a slight (10 percent) reduction in amount fed, with a reasonable increase in exercise would lead to more weight loss and better health than to do nothing but change from the highest calorie food in the table to the lowest.

Table 1 *Comparison, based on bag claims, of four major dry kibble dog foods purchased in a supermarket*

	PURINA	PURINA	IAMS	PEDIGREE
% Crude protein	21	26	24	21
% Fat	10	16	10	10
NFE ("carbs")	43	34	42	44
Weight of bag in pounds	8.8	8.0	8.0	8.8
Cost per bag	$7.29	$10.99	$9.99	$7.49
Cost per pound	$.83	$1.37	$1.25	$.85
Kcal/pound dry matter[3]	1.801	1.987	1.787	1.812
Cost/kcal	$.52	$.78	$.77	$.53

[3] For detailed discussion of energy calculations, see page the Appendix, page 169.

DRY MATTER
A DRY TOPIC, BUT IMPORTANT

Have you ever wondered if dry food is better than canned? Most have a haunting question or two in the back of their minds about the relative benefit of table scraps, or raw foods, or natural diets. When comparing different diets, first, each must be reduced to a 100 percent dry matter basis. This should be intuitive, but it bears explaining because it is so fundamental in its importance. A pound of watermelon does not deliver the same nutrition as a pound of sugar. Same weight, but one is very wet and the other very dry. There is no protein or energy or nutrition of any kind in water. (Okay, trace amount of minerals, sometimes.)

It is commonplace to wonder which of two pet foods is better; better for protein, better for cost, better for overall nutrition. The final and best answer comes from your pet, but at the very beginning of any comparison of different pet foods, there must be a clear understanding of one very basic nutrition fundamental. This is the concept of dry matter: how much water is in the food. Just as for melons and sugar, a pound of dry kibble delivers a different amount of nutrition than a pound of canned food, or a pound of frozen food. There are infinite ways to contrast pet foods; protein amount, protein quality, kind of fat, cooked or raw, level of digestibility, even stool quality. These comparisons and many others are all valid, but without first adjusting for amount of dry matter, they are meaningless.

For some reason, this concept is hard for pet owners to grasp. It seems to land in a blind spot in their comprehension. To which you might reply: it would help if someone would explain it clearly. This would be a fair criticism as it is seldom even explained, let alone clearly. And admittedly, like any fine point of a given pet food's nutrition, it is irrelevant if your endpoint of evaluation of a pet food is simply, "Do I like the way my dog looks and acts?" Despite a lot of scrutiny and discussion about labels, many pet owners rest their rating of a food on animal appearance and behavior. And that is okay. It is what really matters.

But, back to the discussion about comparing products and their label claims. If you are going to engage in this, you must first put each product on a dry matter basis. To illustrate what this means, consider two dog foods on the store shelf, one canned, the other a dry kibble. The label on the can claims 12 percent protein, the bag of kibble 28 percent protein. If on the basis of this information you bought the kibble product because it was higher in protein, you made a big mistake. If the two are compared on a dry matter basis (the only way they can be compared), the canned product is 40 percent protein and the dry kibble 31 percent.

Here's the fine print if one takes just a minute to think about it. By regulation, all pet foods must declare their level of moisture on the label. Just subtract this from 100 to know the dry matter. What is not water in a can of pet food is dry matter.

So, too, for dry food. All dry kibble is 10 percent moisture, thus 90 percent dry matter. What we really want to know in comparing products is: what is the protein in the dry matter in the package, not the protein in the whole package as it sits on the shelf.

Most canned foods are 70 percent moisture, therefore 30 percent dry matter. What we really want to know about the canned pet food we are discussing is: what part of 30 is 12?. It is (12/30 =) .40 or 40 percent. If the label on a can says 70 percent moisture and 12 percent protein, that food is 40 percent protein on a dry matter basis. This simple math (100-10 = 90) applied to a 28 percent protein bag of kibble gives a dry matter protein of 31 percent. (28/90 = .31 or 31 percent)

As just explained for protein, the very same math can be applied to any nutrient, and to any pet food. By nationwide regulation, all pet food must declare moisture on their label. Subtract it from 100 to determine the dry matter. Divide any number on the label by this dry matter to calculate the nutrient on a dry matter basis. Pets with loose stools are a frequent complaint. This problem, 90 percent of the time, is simply feeding too much. A pet owner was feeding two cans of food and switched to an equal weight of dry kibble, resulting in loose stools. Because you have patiently finished reading this, you understand why: two pounds of kibble delivers over three times the dry matter as two cans of food.

DIGESTIBILITY TRIALS

In the U.S. market today, most cans of pet food are not one pound – which is 454 grams – but one fifth less at about 370 grams. By declaring the weight in grams, and hiding behind the move to a metric system, manufacturers avoid having to admit their can is less than the old one pound you were used to. Now once again, in the real world, this issue of dry matter intake is usually not addressed. People tend to feed their pet whatever they last bought at the market and stand back and watch. If the pet gets fat, they feed less (hopefully), and if the pet loses weight, they switch brands.

But professionals have to consider dry matter intake when researching animal nutrition. The most common tool used in research of nutrition is the digestibility trial. It is not a complete investigation in that it leaves some important questions unanswered. But it does address one essential truth: if the food doesn't get from the intestine into the body, it cannot nourish the animal. So the basic approach is to measure what goes into the animal (what it eats) and what comes out (what is excreted in the feces). The difference between these two measurements is what is taken into the animal's body. Remember, a simple digestibility trial says nothing about the fate or value of a food component once absorbed. It is only screening a food to learn if it is absorbed and to what extent. If a food component is not absorbed, or is poorly absorbed, it is of little nutritional value to the animal.

It is possible to learn about each nutrient in a digestibility trial. The food dry matter (remember dry matter!) is assayed for each component of interest. Say our interest is in protein. The percent protein in the food, times the amount of food eaten, yields the amount of protein eaten, or taken in. The same math performed on the feces (dry matter) yields the amount of protein excreted. The difference between these two calculations is the amount of protein absorbed into the body, or the digestibility of the protein in the diet. Similar math can be done on each of the other components, giving a good idea of the diet's usefulness. What one finds is that fat is usually digested at 80 to 95 percent, carbohydrate at about 80 percent, protein at 30 to 90 percent (depending on quality) and minerals at about 30 to 50 percent. These values though, even if carefully calculated, are an estimate.

Technically, there are other factors considered in more exacting research. For example, food moving through the gastrointestinal (usually abbreviated GI) tract scrapes off cells from the intestinal lining, adding protein and fat to the feces. A simple digestibility trial ignores these small adjustments. To accommodate this technicality, any value from a standard digestibility trial is classed more correctly as apparent digestibility. *For more on digestibility trials see End Notes page 163.*

PROTEIN

It may be the advertising industry, pet food companies or the consumer, but among them, they manage to get it wrong in the approach to protein nutrition. Dog food packages, whether they are canned, bagged or frozen, invariably talk about the amount of protein they contain. The consumers, for their part, invariably think the more protein the better. To do so is to ignore a nutrition basic called biologic value. Because of this concept, it is possible for a dog food of 16 percent protein to be of superior nutritional value compared to one that is 38 percent protein. The amount of protein in a food is only part of the story, only half the score of a ball game.

If I told you that the Yankees and the Red Sox were playing and the score was 7, you would look at me either as stupid or soon forthcoming with another number. The reason protein amount is only half the story is because there is another critical dimension to the topic. That is the quality of the protein, or its biologic value. To know the true utility of the protein part of a diet, it is essential to know both the amount of protein and the biologic value of that protein. A pound of nickels and a pound of dimes have identical weight but far different value.

All proteins are made up of building units called amino acids (Table 2). There are 22 of these amino acids found in varying proportions in all proteins. There are other amino acids besides these 22, such as taurine (discussed later), but the vast majority of all proteins are composed of 22 amino acids. Amino acids are small molecules, each containing nitrogen (also referred to as an amide group, hence the name). Amino acids combine by the hundreds and thousands, under the direction of our DNA blueprint, to make protein. Enzymes, which catalyze all our metabolic reactions, are proteins and made of amino acids, at the direction of our genome. As Dr. Rosemary Schraer told her biochemistry classes for years at Penn State, life is just a bowl of enzymes. Even your everyday enzyme can increase the speed of a reaction several thousand-fold.

Amino acids are divided into two types, essential and nonessential. Essential amino acids are dietary necessities and must be in the diet. The nonessential amino acids animals can make for themselves, by assembling them from other components of the diet, given enough other assembly parts.

Table 2 *The common amino acids, the building blocks of all proteins*

Essential (must be in the diet)	Nonessential (can be assimilated from other dietary components)
Isoleucine	Glycine
Leucine	Glutamic Acid
Lysine	Aspartic Acid
Methionine	Proline
Threonine	Alanine
Tryptophan	Serine
Valine	Tyrosine
Histidine	Cysteine
Arginine	Asparagine
Phenylalanine	Hydroxproline
Taurine (cat)	Cystien

It is possible to rank proteins for their nutritional impact, or biologic value (Table 3). For example, the protein in egg is very high quality. This stands to reason in that an egg must become a complete creature with no further input from its mother or anything else. As a matter of fact, egg protein is designated as the highest value protein and all others are compared to it. The reason egg is so high in quality is that its amino acid complement contains more of the essential amino acids than any other protein. The protein of milk is also very high quality, though not quite as high as egg protein. Milk is the sole nourishment for a newborn mammal, and quality is critical. Note that we are saying the protein of egg, and the protein of milk. These foods are not made of just protein as they also contain fat, minerals and carbohydrate, and like most all foods, are a mixture of different nutritional components.

But when considering the protein fraction of these foods, a ranking of them by the quality of their protein is possible. The biologic value of milk is set at 93, meaning it is 93 percent of the value of egg protein, which is the standard and considered 100.

Table 3 *Biologic Value of the proteins in various foods*

These approximate values are all ranked against the protein of egg, the most nutritious protein in nature.	
Egg	100
Milk	93
Rice	86
Fish	75
Beef	75
Casein (one milk protein)	75
Corn	72
Cottonseed flour	60
Peanut flour	56
Wheat gluten	44

The amount of protein in rice is not great, at eight percent or less, but the biologic value of its protein is quite high for a plant, at 86. This is fortunate as a major portion of the world's population derives much of its protein from rice. Below a value of 75, which is where most plant proteins fall, there is a lack of essential amino acids for the proper nourishment of a growing mammal. It is possible, with very careful blending of high quality plant proteins, to formulate a diet that comes fairly close to nutritional adequacy for a young mammal, but the inconvenience of this approach is great. So much so that it is far easier to just include a little milk or egg. Sometimes a quaint analogy is used to illustrate this concept that amino acid make-up defines and limits a protein's quality. Envision an old wooden barrel with staves of varying height (Figure 3). The amount of water the barrel can hold is limited by the height of the shortest stave, just as the quality of a protein is determined by its most limiting amino acid.

So hopefully you see now that a bag of dog food that claims to be 32 percent protein is conceivably no better than one that is only 16 percent. If the 32 percent product is composed of low quality plant proteins, it comes up inferior in essential amino acids to one that is a high percentage milk and egg protein. In the pet food market a 16 percent protein diet containing milk and egg can be quite expensive and, competition being what it is, such a diet would be passed over by the consumer as not only too costly, but from the pet owner's uninformed viewpoint, of less quality than a diet of 32 percent protein.

Figure 3 The Biologic Value of a protein is determined by the amount of the most limiting amino acid, just as the water a barrel will hold is limited by the shortest stave

FAT

Probably no other aspect of nutrition is more cluttered with misinformation than the topic of fat. Because fat is not the evil villain you've been led to believe, a little background is called for to help us understand the correct role of fat in animal nutrition. Fat is an involved topic if it is considered in detail. We will try to keep this discussion simplistic, and begin with the caloric content of fat. Everyone knows fat is an excellent source of calories, and people as well as pets very much enjoy the texture and flavor of fat, and its ability to satisfy hunger. Fat contains nine calories per gram, while carbohydrate and protein each are four. Also, most everyone has at least heard of saturated and unsaturated fat. Plants tend to be the source of the unsaturated fats, and liquid or oil at room temperature, while animal fat tends to be more of the saturated kind, and solid at room temperature. Think corn oil and bacon fat. Fat from swine is referred to as lard, from cattle as tallow. Poultry fat is called poultry fat, and fat from sheep is called mutton tallow. A lipid's melting point (lipid means fat) is determined, among other things, by its chemical structure and principally by the hydrogen content. Saturated and unsaturated denote relative amounts of hydrogen. In simplistic terms, a saturated fat is holding all the hydrogen it can (saturated with hydrogen), while an unsaturated fat has room for more hydrogen. It is possible to add more hydrogen to an unsaturated fat, a process called hydrogenation. This alters melting point—or whether or not the fat is a solid or liquid at room temperature.

Fats of concern to us at the moment are arranged in a molecule referred to as a triglyceride, also called triacylglycerol. A triglyceride is a molecule of glycerol, which is three carbon atoms in a row, each carbon with a fatty acid attached. There are also mono and diglycerides—glycerol with one or two fatty acids attached. Fatty acids are the building blocks of lipids, somewhat the same way that amino acids are the sub-units of protein, and there are about a dozen more common fatty acids (Table 4). Fatty acids have a backbone of carbon atoms arranged in a chain, and they are designated by the number of carbons in the chain, which almost always is an even number.

Most of the information and misinformation on lipid nutrition of the past half century has centered around the fatty acids of longer chain length, from 16 to 18 carbons, their level of saturation, and their effect on hardening of the arteries. Inasmuch as atherosclerosis is not a major concern in animal nutrition, you will be spared the details of that drama. The discussion about omega-3 and omega-6 fatty acids, those of 18, 20 and 22 carbon chain length, is pertinent, and this topic will be covered in detail in Chapter 10 under Nutraceuticals.

Table 4 *Common Fatty Acids of Foods.*

Common Name	Number Of Carbons: double bonds
Short Chain	
Acetic	2:0
Propionic	3:0
Butyric	4:0
Caproic	6:0
Caprylic	8:0
Medium Chain	
Capric	10:0
Lauric	12:0
Saturated (no double bonds, full of hydrogen)	
Myristic	14:0
Palmitic	16:0
Stearic	18:0
Unsaturated (one or more double bonds, room for more hydrogen)	
Palmitoleic	16:1
Oleic	18:1
Linoleic	18:2
Linolenic*	18:3
Arachadonic	20:4
Eicosapentaenoic*	20:5

Common Name	Number Of Carbons: double bonds
Docosahexaenoic*	22:6

These fatty acids are of the omega-3 configuration and their lack in the diet has been incriminated in the cause of various afflictions.

Most plant material tends to range from three to eight percent fat. But plant seeds and fruits, such as pine nuts or avocados, can be quite high in fat. Some grain by-products, such as rice bran, can be 10 to 12 percent. Expanded dog foods, the kibble so common in the market, are composed mostly of plant ingredients and dry meat by-products. To improve nutrition and appeal to the pet, fat is frequently an added ingredient, both in the formula mix, and sprayed on after the kibble is made. But fat has a tendency to oxidize or become rancid, a type of spoilage that has a bad effect on flavor, and can also leave an unpleasant aftertaste. Consequently, all fats contain antioxidants to prevent oxidation and rancidity. These antioxidants by law must be disclosed on the label and some of them are BHA (butylated hydroxylanisole), BHT (butylated hydroxytoluene) and propyl galate.

Most consumers consider these chemicals as a negative, and producers have been researching methods to eliminate these preservatives. Vitamin E is a very good antioxidant, as is citric acid. But to date, natural antioxidant systems are still less effective, and it is only fair to expect a genuine and honest "all natural" pet food to have a shorter shelf life than one with conventional fat preservatives. Said another way, if a bag of "all natural" pet food is stored in the attic for three months in the summer, and it is not rancid, it probably wasn't all natural.

Because fat contains over twice the calories of protein and carbohydrate, a little fat in a formula adds calories quickly. As seen in the example in Table 1 in the Appendix, fat, at 10 percent on the label claim, was less than protein or carbohydrate, but was the source of almost 25 percent of the calories. If fat on the label claim had been 18 percent instead of 10 percent, still less than either protein or carbohydrate, it would have contributed 42 percent of the calories. But as we'll see, calories from fat are not the culprit everyone thinks, and indeed, raising fat can be a means of lowering carbohydrate, which can actually make for a less fattening diet, if done correctly. This is one of the concepts espoused by the Atkins Diet and the Zone Diet, two popular nutrition programs for people.

FIBER

Fiber is another example of a nutrition topic that refuses to lend itself to a tidy discussion in one sitting. Fiber rightfully belongs in the nutritional category of carbohydrate, but because simple stomached animals (such as dogs and cats) can't digest fiber, it is usually considered in a separate discussion. Fiber is integral to a discussion about bacteria, and also anatomy. To cover the topic of fiber correctly in any one section is to steal thunder belonging in other sections. Well, perhaps dietary fiber is not a thunderous topic, but you get what I mean. Provided here are the basics, with further discussion intermittent throughout the book.

Classifying the different digestive systems of animals tends to parallel the relationship an animal has with bacteria. In broad terms, the world is divided into monogastrics and herbivores. Monogastrics, as the word implies, have one stomach. People and dogs and cats are monogastrics.

Herbivores typically have the adaptation of a large holding area at some point in the first half of the tract that serves as a fermentation tank where bacteria break down the plant fibers. But as a class they are so diverse in their feeding strategies and anatomy that they almost don't exist as a class. As a group, herbivores include cattle, sheep, goats, deer, horses and rabbits to mention a few of the more obvious. This group also includes elephants, certain primates (so called leaf eaters) kangaroos, wildebeest and gazelles, to mention some that might not occur to you. The main reason the classification is so large is because the world's land mass is covered with plants that perpetually capture the sun's energy, and are an unfailing meal if you can survive on them. Drought of course can be a problem, but there are adaptations for this, such as migration. Because plants are so reliable, evolution favored the ascendance of animals that could survive using plants as their food. Because plants are so ubiquitous and abundant, there are lots of animals that eat them. Because plants are not particularly dense in concentrations of protein or energy, herbivores have spacious gastrointestinal (GI) tract adaptations to allow the consumption of large amounts of plants. An 1,100 pound herbivore on the Serengeti Plains will devour up to 150 pounds of forage in a day.

No mammal produces an enzyme that will act on plant fiber. However, most all mammals have GI tract bacteria that afford some fiber breakdown for the benefit of their host, with some really good at it. Table 5 shows that cattle and sheep (well, their bacteria, actually) are very good fiber digesters, while man and dog are far less accomplished.

But man, dog and even the carnivorous cat derive some benefit from fiber. Another point illustrated by Table 5 is the location of where the fiber digestion happens. In the horse it is mostly in the colon (large intestine) while in the capybara it is in the cecum (called the appendix in humans) or the rumen in the cow or deer. Leaf eating monkeys have stomach partitions that aid fiber digestion. The variability of fiber digestion in mammals is broad, from 17 to 83 percent, and the only generalization we can make is animals that survive as plant eaters digest at least 50 percent of the fiber they consume.

According to the late Dr. John Tracy, up to half of a swine's maintenance needs can be met with energy derived from fiber breakdown by hind gut fermentation. Remember, maintenance energy needs are only what is required by an adult to walk around and breathe. To gestate, nurse young or enable growth requires in some cases as much as twice the energy as simple maintenance. We know that modern man can digest up to 17 percent fiber in the diet, due of course to the bacteria in the large intestine, so conceivably ancient man did even better, maybe even approaching the levels seen in the pig.

Table 5 *Mammalian fermentation capacity expressed as a percentage of total possible tract fermentation. P.J. Van Soest, 1994. Nutritional Ecology of the Ruminant, p59.*

Species	Rumen	Cecum	Colon	Total
Sheep	71	8	4	83
Capybara	-	71	9	80
Cattle	64	5	6	75
Horse	-	15	54	69
Guinea Pig	-	46	20	66
Rat	-	32	29	61
Rabbit	-	43	8	51
Pig	-	15	33	48
Human	-	-	17	17
Cat	-	-	16	16
Dog	-	1	13	14

A fiber discussion is a great opportunity to tie together some broad nutrition concepts. Powered by energy from the sun, in a process we all know as photosynthesis, the plant kingdom takes carbon dioxide from the air and uses it to make sugar, starch, cellulose and other fibers, and returns the oxygen part of the carbon dioxide to the air.

The basic building block of cellulose and starch is the sugar called glucose. Glucose is ubiquitous in nature and is the same molecule that is the coin of energy metabolism for all animals. Glucose is a chain of six carbons and an oxygen, closed into a circle or ring. When many sugar units are linked together, they are called polysaccharides; two sugar units are called disaccharides; one is a monosaccharide. Cellulose, a polysaccharide, is the most abundant organic compound in the world. In cellulose, glucose units are linked together by a bond referred to as β1,4 (beta 1,4) which bacterial, but not mammalian, enzymes can break. Starch is many glucose units linked by bonds called α1,4 (alpha 1,4) and α1,6. Starch made of straight chains of glucose is called amylose, and uses α1,4 bonds. Starch chains with branches, called amylopectin, use an α1,6 bond at the branch site. Mammalian enzymes can break these bonds.

Fiber is actually a class of compounds that includes cellulose, hemicellulose, lignin, lignocellulose and pectins, to name the more abundant fiber categories. Animal nutritionists speak in terms of acid detergent fiber and neutral detergent fiber as a way of partitioning fiber according to cell wall or cell content, and its relative digestibility by bacteria. The other fibers are likewise indigestible, except to a minor degree by bacteria. Chitin, the exoskeleton of insects and crabs, and part of my early research on feeding cockroaches to cows, is a polysaccharide. It, too, is a chain of glucose units, and, incidentally, second only to cellulose in abundance in the world. *For more on chitin, see End Notes page 165.*

All the fruits and vegetables we eat contain fiber to one extent or another. I have always felt that the leaves around an artichoke heart were an inordinate amount of penance to endure to get to the heart of the artichoke, which I found delectable. If you ever took the time and effort to eat an artichoke leaf, you will recall it required a great deal of serious chewing and yielded small returns. Maybe that is why artichokes are always served with some sort of sinful dip, to distract us from the pedestrian taste of all those leaves. Fiber is what makes artichoke leaves the way they are, and if you ate several of them, nothing bad would happen. In fact, fiber, or bulk as it is sometimes called, has a beneficial effect on the GI tract. Besides adding bulk to the stool, the abrasive effect helps renew the cell lining of the intestine.

The biomedical literature on fiber is vast, and tends to show that fiber in the diet is beneficial. Lack of fiber is associated with increased incidence of problems of all sorts, such as colon cancer and high cholesterol, but one must be careful about going too far with this information. Keep in mind that the beneficial effect of fiber may be that it dilutes energy in the diet (a good thing) and it lessens soluble carbohydrate (another good thing). In this way, our pets (including cats) benefit from fiber, so don't shy away from this component of their diet. As long as their diet is providing all the other nutrients they require, fiber can be quite high, meaning up to 15 or even 20 percent of the diet dry matter. The thing you need to guard against is the inclusion of fiber in a diet to the exclusion of other necessary and more expensive ingredients.

Animals that derive life-sustaining nourishment from fiber represent what in nature is called a symbiotic relationship – a mutually dependent and beneficial coexistence. The bacteria in these animals get a warm place to live, sheltered from all storms, and are handed a meal every day – the forage the herbivore consumes. In return, they partially digest this meal, sending their leavings on to the host, as well as the metabolic by-products of their own metabolism. All mammalian GI tracts harbor bacteria.

From there, animal digestive systems divide into those with friendly and helpful fiber digesting bacteria predominating in the far end, like dogs' or ours, and others that have friendly and essential bacteria predominantly in the front, such as herbivores.

We need to look a little closer at the division made between monogastric and herbivore. In introductory animal nutrition the student is sometimes left with the impression that herbivores are teeming with bacteria in their gut and monogastrics are devoid of bacteria. The demarcation is not at all that clear. In fact, the pig, a classic monogastric, as mentioned earlier, can digest a measurable amount of fiber in its diet, and so can people. Fiber digestion in monogastrics is done by bacteria in the large intestine. The gorilla in the wild must certainly digest some fiber, given that their diet is very similar to that of a herbivore. People can digest up to 17 percent of the fiber they ingest. Ruminants digest 70 to 80 percent. Monogastrics are not that big a flop at fiber digestion, and herbivores are not all that superb at it. As a matter of fact, there are numerous examples in nature of animals with digestive physiology in between ruminant and monogastric. The horse lacks the paunch or fore stomach of a true ruminant, but has an enlarged cecum and colon that do the same job, in the same way, in symbiosis with bacteria. The Colobus monkey of Africa, and Langurs of Asia, that live almost exclusively in trees and are sometimes referred to as leaf eaters, have what is called a complex stomach, which is an adaptation to a high fiber diet, and also takes advantage of symbiosis with bacteria.

In Australia, a truly fascinating laboratory of Darwinian evolution, there were no traditional herbivores, so this void in the ecological niche was filled by the kangaroo and its relatives. When sport loving European immigrants introduced rabbits to Australia for their hunting pleasure, escapees nearly overran the subcontinent with progeny. The ecosystem was completely unprepared to provide a check on the rabbit population. This little herbivore found itself in a paradise devoid of nearly all enemies, save maybe the immigrant sportsmen, who evidently were inept marksmen.

I love the following story. It actually happened. Well, the facts are quite disconcerting, I don't love that part, but it is a classic example of how evolution perfects a species and the absolutely critical role of the odd duck or outlier of a gene pool. This tale belongs in Chapter 4 discussing adaptability, but fits here too. It is retold here from *Down Under* by Bill Bryson (Transworld Publishers, London, 2000).

In 1859, Thomas Austin imported 24 English rabbits into Australia for his sport hunting pleasure. The Australian ecosystem had kangaroos as the pinnacle herbivore and had never seen rabbits. The rabbits thus found themselves in a paradise without any enemies—of any kind, carnivore or bacterial. They multiplied with abandon, as only rabbits can. Within 20 years two million acres of Victoria had been mowed clean by the voracious rabbit herd. Things got worse as the rabbits expanded their territory 75 miles a year, and a severe drought set in. Domestic livestock producers suffered the most, as range land became barren and useless, irreparably ruined in some cases.

A solution was found from South America, in a virus called myxomatosis. It was viciously lethal for a rabbit but harmless to anything else. Soon the countryside was literally covered with dead rabbit as 999 of every 1000 succumbed. It seemed a miracle cure (from the people's point of view). Only one rabbit in 1000 survived. But that was enough. The reason they survived was because they were immune to the virus, and these few rabbits resumed the march of the species imperative, to get genes into the next generation. In time, Australia was once again awash in rabbits.

In 2002 a popular film came out, called *Rabbit Proof Fence*, which was not about rabbits, but the travails of young native Australians in the 1930s trying to walk home along a 1,500 mile fence. This fence was built to control rabbits that once again were inundating the countryside. Due to the genius of the laws of evolution, the rabbits had adapted around near total destruction, becoming impervious to a deadly virus. Such perfecting goes on millions of times a day in millions of species, and has for billions of years.

CARBOHYDRATES

Photosynthesis by plants combines the carbon of carbon dioxide into different sugars that serve the plant in different ways. A college dean in Mexico City once told me a simplistic and delightful observation. If you are in the business of agriculture, you are in the business of harvesting sunshine and water. I was enthralled with this wisdom, even though a bit embarrassed that I had never heard it or thought of it myself. It is a fundamental and basic truth. The only question after this is in what form will you market your harvest? Will it be meat or milk, or fiber for clothing like cotton or wool, or avocados or sugar? It could be any one of dozens of products, and they all are either plants or made possible by plants.

The plants combine the carbon into carbohydrates used for three types of compounds: sugars, starches and fiber. Depending on our intentions, we harvest a plant based on its carbohydrate components. Trees, high in the fibers cellulose and lignin, are harvested for use as timber, paper and firewood. Corn and wheat are used for their starch content, while sugar cane and beets are sources of sucrose, or table sugar. With virtually every plant harvested for one specific reason, there are a few to several byproducts from each plant. The production of wheat flour, for example, has many byproducts flowing from the mill, such as wheat bran, wheat mill run, and first, second and third clears, not to mention the straw left in the field. All have economic value, with many used in pet foods. The main reason for growing cotton is for fiber for clothes, but byproducts of this endeavor include seeds and high protein meal used for animal feeds, seed hulls used in oil drilling muds and for animal feed, oil used in cooking, and cotton burrs, also called gin trash, used for animal feed.

In both plants and animals, energy can be stored in the form of carbohydrates. Plants use starch. Seeds are preloaded with starch as part of a species survival strategy to get the plant genes into the next generation. Starch serves as the source of energy for the tiny seedling until it is capable of photosynthesis on its own. This concentrated energy content of seeds was perceived by man in Mesopotamia 10,000 years ago, and was the impetus for modern agriculture.

The animal world also stores some energy in carbohydrate, in a molecule called glycogen. Glycogen is similar to starch, with the same type of bonds between the glucose units, but there are about three times more branches in glycogen. Glycogen is found in muscle and liver. Liver concentration is higher per unit of weight, but total body stores are more in the muscle because there is more muscle than liver in an animal. Pets do not encounter a great deal of glycogen because meat is not a common ingredient of dry pet foods, and glycogen levels in meat are normally less than one percent. Liver is not an uncommon ingredient in canned foods, but even in liver, glycogen stores average less than five percent. However, if and when glycogen is encountered in food, it is easily digested and processed to glucose units.

Sucrose or table sugar is a disaccharide, being a molecule of glucose and a molecule of fructose. It goes without saying that sucrose is digestible by mammals. Maltose is another disaccharide, composed of two glucose molecules, and it derives mainly from the hydrolysis (breakdown) of starch. Lactose is the disaccharide found almost exclusively in milk, made of one glucose and one galactose, and all mammalian young have the enzyme needed for its digestion. This enzyme, called lactase, can grow quiescent in some adults, with the consequence that milk or dairy products high in lactose can cause some people to have digestive upset. Age related metabolic switches are not unusual. For example, gray hair is common in adults, but never in children.

It is presumed that the gene for lactase persistence in humans came into existence about the time cattle were domesticated, and it is the most rapidly spreading gene mutation yet discovered. Evidently, it is a second gene, or set of genes, that keeps the gene for lactase production switched on. Since the 1960s, anthropologists have been aware that groups of humans that raise cattle also tend to be the ones who can drink milk as adults. In a 2006 article in *Nature* by Erika Check, it was reported that researchers had shown that in African cattle herding peoples, lactase persistence arose between 3,000 and 7,000 years ago, and spread quickly. As pointed out in this article, the researchers said for a gene mutation to have spread that quickly, it had to have conferred a great survival advantage. There was a similar mutation in Northern Europeans, even sooner.

Starch, when heated in water, undergoes a process called gelatinization. This is not reversible, like frying an egg (you can't unfry an egg), and is a universal step in cooking. Think pie crust, donut, cracker, cookie, pasta. These will be recognized as rather dry forms of starch, although I suppose many would argue that donuts are decidedly not dry. Starch is also a universal thickening agent seen in foods like tapioca and gravy. The property of starch to expand when gelatinized, and retain its shape and hardness when cooled and dried, is used by the pet food industry to make dry kibble. The machine used for this, called an extruder, forces a food mixture through a long barrel by means of a screw running inside the length of the barrel (Figure 4).

DRY & WET INGREDIENTS

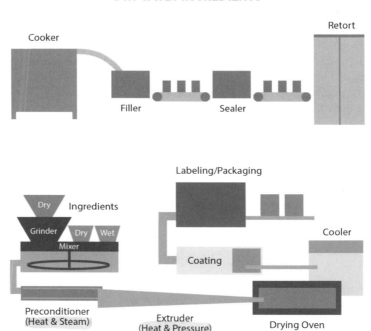

Figure 4 *Schematic of a machinery line to make canned food (above) and dry kibble.*

The tolerances are very close between the screw and the barrel's inside wall, such that when the screw is rotated at high rpm, great heat is generated and the food cooked to a high temperature for a short time. When leaving the heat and pressure of the barrel as it exits, the starch component of the food expands and is promptly cooled. There is a minimum starch level required in the food for extrusion to be successful, with the result that most extruded (or expanded as they are sometimes called) pet foods are up to half starch or soluble carbohydrate of some kind. Extrusion is an economic way to make dry pet foods, leading a lot of large breed owners to rely on expanded foods to keep costs low. The problem with this is that dogs fed only expanded kibble consume a constant and high amount of soluble carbohydrate, which as we've discussed may have health repercussions over a lifetime. It sure seems to be so in people.

Nearly half of Americans are overweight. In a New York Times best seller, *Water for Elephants* by Sara Gruen, there is a picture of the freak show contingent of an early 20th century era circus. There is the requisite dwarf, bearded lady, giant, etc., and the fat lady. The thing that caught my attention about the fat lady is that she would hardly qualify for a freak show today. People (both men and women) of her heft and beam are to be seen by the dozens in any public place. There is a bundle of afflictions and symptoms that comes with obesity that the medical profession refers to as metabolic syndrome. These include high blood pressure, elevated cholesterol, hardening of the arteries and prediabetes traits. The cover story of *Business Week* of August 6, 2007 stated that 40 percent of American dogs are overweight. It strikes me as no coincidence that obesity in dogs exactly equals that seen in people.

By now you appreciate that when you buy a bag of dog food or a can of cat food, it is some blend of protein, fat, carbohydrate, water and minerals, but you are still wondering, what is the best blend for my pet, what is the right diet? We discussed energy and its different ways of being measured. We talked about protein quality and how it is just as important as amount of protein. We've set the stage for a clearer take on fat, especially in contrast to soluble carbohydrate, and we covered the all-important concept of dry matter in a diet. This chapter, cumbersome as it was, is the last of the drudgery for now. With the rules and definitions in place, we are now going to take a look back at what was food in time past. It might help us understand what should be food today.

REFERENCES

sled dogs burn 11,000 calories... Case LP, Carey DP, Hirakawa DA, Dristotle L. 2000. Canine and Feline Nutrition. A Resource for Companion Animal Professionals. Mosby, Inc. St. Louis, Mo. 63146. Page 266.

lactase persistence gene spread quickly... Check E. 2006. How Africa Learned to Love the Cow. Nature, Vol. 444, Dec 21/28. Page 994.

similar mutation in Europeans... Cochran, G., and H Harpening. 2009. The 10,000 Year Explosion. How civilization accelerated human evolution. Basic Books, Philadelphia, PA 19103. Page 77.

picture of the freak show... Gruen, S. 2006. Water for Elephants. Algonquin books of Chapel Hill. Chapel Hill, NC. 27515.

cover story of business week... Brady D, Palmeri C. 2007. The Pet Economy. In: business Week, August 6, 2007.

in End Notes: equations for estimating energy needs... NRC 2006. Nutrient Requirements of Dogs and Cats. 2006. National Research Council. National Academies press. Washington, DC. 20001.

3

THE PRIMORDIAL DIET
(JUST WHAT ARE MAMMALS PERFECTED TO THRIVE ON?)

What we shall consider now is just what did the world offer for animals to eat. What was the nature of food options when mammals were making their long march towards the present? All would concede that oxygen, carbon and hydrogen go back a long way. Basic molecular structure has never changed. Critical molecules, such as amino acids, enzymes and hormones are found largely unchanged throughout all of biology. Stromatolites, primordial stacks of fossilized cells found as far apart as the Australian outback and the Canadian Shield, lived over 3,500 million years ago. Cytochrome C, a group of copper containing enzymes, is one of the most highly conserved compounds—meaning found everywhere—in all of biology. Cytochrome C is in the mitochondria of all eukaryotic cells, which is to say everywhere. Anything evolved beyond a bacterium or algae has cells that are eukaryotic.

We can't be certain that the amino acid lysine of today is the same as lysine from three billion years ago. One report compared 3,000 year old barley from archeological sites with 40 to 150 year old barley and found them "remarkably similar" with lysine and methionine slightly lower in modern barley. DNA itself has not been found older than 30,000 years. Ever increasing analytical sophistication will one day prove what is only intuitive for now, that mammalian metabolism of today is faithfully descendent from millions of years ago. The following discussion is based on the hypothesis that what animals ate millions of years ago is still available today.

The scientific literature doesn't offer much insight about diet prior to the advent of crop husbandry 10,000 years ago. There is scholarly and informed insight in greater abundance for the period from 10,000 years ago to the present, and obviously it becomes easier to connect the dots the closer one gets to the present. Archeologists, to their credit, are renowned for plundering other technologies and science fields. With just a few crucial bone fragments, archeologists can sketch in an entire skeleton, know its sex, age at death, and medical history. It is absolutely amazing what a tooth, not to mention a jaw bone, says to a trained archeologist. And that is just with the aid of a magnifying glass or microscope. By means of isotope ratio analysis (the amount of 12C compared to 14C) archeologists can speculate with good confidence about the time period of the past when an animal or plant lived. [For more on radio carbon dating, see *End Notes page 165.*

Now even more advanced analytical methods afford insight based on the ratios of 12C and 13C, another isotope of carbon that is stable and does not decay. This information permits a glimpse of insight about diet, which when considered with other factors, allows some careful assumptions. An example would be coprolites, or fossilized feces, that reveal what someone or some animal ate. The modern day division of archeology that studies coprolites gathers minute shreds of data from all over the world and patches together useful insight. To the extent that these feces can be deconstructed and analyzed, things can be learned that infer facts about long ago diets.

Examples of such other factors would be the age of the sediment surrounding the particular piece of evidence, or records from elsewhere of what the world and its climate were doing at the time. An illustration would be the mass extinction of 65 million years ago, accepted as having been wrought by a meteor that hit the Yucatan in easternmost Mexico. Meteors are a rich and unique source of the element iridium, and everywhere in the world, there is a thin layer of sediment in the 65 million year old rocks that is greatly elevated in its content of iridium. Beneath this layer, there are many fossil species that cease to be found when you look above this layer. This makes possible the hypothesis that a meteor struck the earth 65 million years ago and many species became extinct at that time.

By similar data analysis, archeologists can make informed speculations about what the world was like in the past, and we can use their teachings to help us understand many things about the primordial diet of the ancient world. In this regard, there tends to be a remarkable symmetry between what the world offers as food and what its creatures require as food. Numerous realities of the primordial world tended to keep an organism evolving on the path to adequate nutrition.

WHO ATE WHO AND WHAT

Everyone is aware of the so-called food chain, with many species and vast herds of herbivores eating plants and a few carnivores eating herbivores. Carnivores need vitamin E, but they get it from their prey—invariably herbivores, who have spent several days consuming plants full of vitamin E. When the carnivore eats the gazelle, he enjoys a conveniently prepared collection of vitamin E (of the most potent form, biologically) and all other plant nutrients such as phytols, pigments, antioxidants. The victim invited to the carnivore's dinner table is eaten entirely. This includes the contents of its GI system, rich in plant material. The image of a carnivore subsisting on only meat and blood is about as incorrect as a myth can be (Figures 5 and 6).

Figure 5 *Herbivores harvest large amounts of plants.*

Figure 6 *Carnivores harvest small amounts of herbivores.*

In the ocean, the base of the food chain is one cell plankton, the phytoplankton, serving in the role of plants on land, taking in carbon dioxide and making cellular material in a process called carbon fixing. Phytoplankton live in the narrow top layer of the sea, where the sun's light can penetrate. Zooplankton dine on plankton, and they in turn are eaten by krill, little fellows about one inch long when mature. Krill are dinner for small fish, in their turn eaten by bigger fish. Seals eat the bigger fish and killer whales eat the seals. Or, the baleen whale just cuts out all the middle men and eats krill. A baleen whale, or Blue Whale, is the largest mammal on earth, and with specialized mouth and teeth, lives its entire life feasting exclusively on the smaller creatures in the sea, the krill. Most of life in the sea is ultimately based on plankton. Deeper layers subsist on the detritus of the upper layers. So it doesn't matter if you dine at the top, the middle or bottom, the benefit is the same. Land or sea, no species has evolved to need some exotic or weird nutrient. Those that took that path were never seen again.

A topic of direct bearing on the nutrition of animals throughout the ages is the fact that daily nourishment was selected from what was at hand at the moment, which could vary, and this selecting influenced the composition of what was eaten. Selection and its influence on diet can be illustrated in this manner. If one were to assay the fresh forage from a field, with random samples taken every 30 feet, the aggregate would represent a very close approximation of the true average composition of the plants in the field. If one were to assay the stomach contents of a horse grazing that same field, you would find the protein and digestibility of the stomach contents was above the field average, and the fiber value below the field average. The wild horse does little else in its day besides eat and make babies. They are very proficient at both. When grazing, like any herbivore, they are instinctively responding to premonitions of what is more delectable and what is less so, resulting in an enhancement of the quality of the nourishment taken in.

People have long ago lost any conscience awareness of what is good for them and what needs to be sought out from the environment and selected as food. Animals still have this ability, in varying degrees. The rat is a pro at it. Given a choice of a diet adequate in lysine content, or only 100 parts per million below adequate, the rat always selects the adequate diet.

There is another point that has bearing on this topic of the primordial diet, and who ate what. Vertebrates can hide or run from their predators or otherwise employ different defense moves. Plants do not have mobility, so they have perfected a different system, noxious chemicals and toxins. Think marijuana, cocaine, caffeine, nicotine, just to name a few of the better known plants' chemicals.

One time I had a pair of my New Mexico horses with a band of local horse at Two Ocean Pass in Wyoming. The first night, all were grazing together in the same meadow. One of my horses started rolling, which horses enjoy doing from time to time, especially when you get off their back. But this one did not stop. Upon inspection, he was sweating and shaking. We stood him in the stream and soon his symptoms abated. Not long after, my other horse went through the same scenario. We spent the following week in that country, and the incident never happened again. My horses, being new to the flora of Wyoming high country, had eaten a plant containing noxious chemicals of some kind. But with one quick lesson, they were as wise as the local horses, none of which took ill, despite grazing within feet of my horses. It must be assumed that all mammals retain some measure of this quick study aptitude, for without it, dining, and therefore life, would be fraught with dire complications.

IN THE SCIENCE OF NUTRITION, ENOUGH IS PLENTY

If you are lacking in water, drinking is a big help. But once proper hydration is achieved, more water does not help. If an animal is deficient in selenium, adding selenium to the diet is useful. Once repletion of the selenium need has been accomplished, additional selenium above the daily need is useless. Adding more selenium is starting into the realm of overdose. Indeed, excess selenium can be harmful. Related to this point is the ancient insight, the poison is in the size of the dose. Selenium for most all mammals is needed in the diet at about 0.3 ppm (parts per million). It is essential, and much less than this, in due time, causes problems to show up. But, this dose is also very tiny. So tiny in fact, that if you had one pound of selenium, you would have enough to feed yourself for over 2,000 years. Nickel is another trace mineral needed in miniscule amounts, and poisonous in excess. Arsenic, the fabled toxin of many a mystery thriller, is a proven essential nutrient for several species, and is suspected to be needed by humans at the level of about 12 micrograms a day. If 12 micrograms is the human daily requirement, a pound of arsenic would last one person 100,000 years. Arsenic is needed, but in ever so tiny amounts. Again, the poison is in the size of the dose. Too much of anything is not good for you. Even ice cream.

The point here is this. Mammals need selenium at about 0.3 ppm because that is about what the earth's crust contains. True, a few soil geographies are deficient, and plants grown on them do not accumulate enough selenium for the mammals that eat solely these plants for months or years. (Modern marketing virtually assures every animal is exposed to feed and grain from numerous different locales.) But for all of the world's creatures, with very rare exception, their surroundings provide all they need. They always have. It was simply impossible for a species to evolve that needed something their surroundings failed to provide. If a species had a gene mutation that caused its vitamin E requirement to increase to 2,000 IU per day, and the best the environment offered was 500 IU per day, that species quickly became extinct.

In decades of feeding different animals all over the world, thinking long and hard about what they needed, and how to get it to them, it began to dawn on me that there were really only a few variations on the theme. If you reduced the needs of a whitetail deer and an elephant to a dry matter basis, the diet composition that nourished one would nourish the other, down to the last molecule. The correct diet for a domestic cat and a Bengal tiger are identical in composition. As a matter of fact, a diet designed for one carnivore will be adequate nutrition for all carnivores, from Alaskan eagle to African lion.

Of all the known nutrients, vitamins, minerals, trace minerals, cofactors or micro-nutrients, all animals need all of them, and invariably, in the same relative order of magnitude in the diet. There are a few exceptions, discussed next, but the commonality of nutrient needs of all creatures is by far the norm. Usually, even the exceptions aren't really exceptions.

Millions of years ago, before Africa and South America drifted apart, there were primates of common ancestry on this geography. Over the eons, a small difference showed up between Old World primates and New World primates. Vitamin D is commercially available as D2 or D3. New world primates must have D3 whereas old world primates can use D3 or consume D2 and convert it to D3. It would appear that cats, and to some extent all carnivores, need an amino acid called taurine whereas dogs can make enough from other precursors. It is accepted thinking that sheep and llamas require less copper than other animals, to the point where they can possibly suffer copper toxicity on feeds adequate for other animals.

Most creatures are able to synthesize their own vitamin C. Humans, great apes and guinea pigs would appear to be an exception, needing preformed vitamin C in the diet. However, with the elucidation of the human genome, it has recently been learned that humans and great apes have the all the necessary genes for making vitamin C, but the terminal step has been turned off. What looks at first glance to be a weakness in evolution's logic is seen to be completely sensible when considered carefully. Nature does not waste resources metabolizing into existence what is already plentiful in the diet. This is considered again in Chapter 10 on vitamins. Another example of the very same principle is cats and their "need" for taurine. Their primordial diet, eaten for millions of years, provides adequate taurine. On dry expanded plant based diets taurine must be supplemented. This is our doing with domestication of the cat, not the failing of the cat or evolution.

CHEMICAL ANALYSIS OF FOODS EATEN

Permit a sneak peek at where this discussion is going. Figure 7 illustrates the possible range of a given nutritional component of a random food item selected from the primordial world. Fat can be found as low as two percent or as high as 60 percent. Protein ranges from four percent in mature hay to over 60 percent in some eggs and seeds. What is striking when foods are considered in this way is the near absence of carbohydrate. There just is very little starch or sugar to be found in nature. Fruit is high if it is dried, but dried fruit is not encountered by hunter gatherers. Table 6 presents the same idea a different way.

Figure 7 *Analysis of any primordial food would show a very wide ranging composition, except for carbohydrate, rarely found above seven percent*

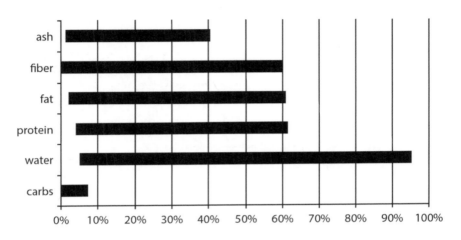

Table 6 *Amount (%) of soluble carbohydrate (starch + sugar) in different foods*

Food	Soluble Carbohydrate (Starch + Sugar), %
Meat and fish	1
Nuts	1-2
Insects	1
Fruits	6-8
Honey	40
Milk	3
Vegetables	4
AVERAGE	3% (without honey, 7% with honey)

Let's take a closer look. What was the analysis of things eaten by mammals for nourishment? Most people have heard of the skeleton known as Lucy, an adolescent female who lived about 3.1 million years ago. She is classed by anthropologists as a member of *Australopithecus afarensis*, usually listed, thankfully, as *A. Afarensis*. Lucy was found in 1974 in Ethiopia by Donald Johanson and Tom Gray, and she created quite a stir due to her candidacy, at least in the eyes of the popular press, as the missing link. Long ago when Lucy and her fellow hominids awoke to begin their day on the plains of Africa, they probably confronted a day spent looking for food. Plant options that we know of were leaves, tender shoots of grass and the pith of plant stalks, nuts and seeds, berries, fruit, roots and tubers, fungi and mushrooms, and gourds or squash. Basically, a lot like the produce aisle at the grocery store. Animal options were, in addition to small animals and amphibians, birds, eggs (bird and reptile), insects (all stages), fish and shell fish, and maybe an occasional large mammal. Possibly there was the proverbial manna of the wandering Israelite fame. Bedouins in the Sinai today still harvest this source of sweet nourishment. This was the secretions of a small insect on the leaves of the tamarisk tree that could be gathered in the morning.

Beet sugar, the source of at least half the table sugar in the modern US, was discovered in 1747. Cane sugar was known in India, where it originated, at least 1000 BC, but was considered a medicine. The Moors introduced sugar cane to Spain during their occupation of the Iberian Peninsula in the eighth century, but cane sugar was not very well known until coffee and tea grew in popularity in Europe after the discovery of the New World.

The only source of concentrated soluble carbohydrate known to exist throughout much of the temperate world, contemporaneously with mammal's evolution, was honey. Biblical references to it are numerous, and Egyptian art is unequivocal that bees were domesticated and managed for the harvest of honey. Both Greeks and Romans knew honey well and wrote about it often. Today, primitive people all over the world harvest honey whenever they can. Interestingly, all seem to appreciate that smoke is an effective and essential aid in robbing hives. These examples of honey in man's diet are all from within the last 10,000 years, or since the dawn of recorded history, and as such are not proof that man in prehistory used honey. But it is hard to imagine he did not. Bears relish honey. When a black bear robs a bee-hive, he is acting out a very ancient imperative. It is a safe assumption that many Pliocene mammals ate honey on the spot whenever they could find it, provided they could counter or tolerate the bee's aggressive defense. A report in the popular press on a discovery by researchers at Oregon State University indicates bees may-be 100 million years old.

We have a list of what was eaten, and we presume it provided for the nourishment of ancient mammals. This presumption is based on the observable fact that species thrived, reproduced and exist to this day. What is left to consider then is the analysis of these foods, both for what they provided, and for what they did not provide. This knowledge, when contrasted with modern diets, should be informative.

Table 7 (shown below in abbreviated format, with a more expanded format in the Appendix, page 178) lists the analysis of some of the food types we eat today and some modern day foods presumed to be available to prehistoric mammals. It is rarely possible to know the exact analysis of what prehistoric mammals ate. We do know that the corn plant of today is much evolved from the one found in ancient caves in the Americas, and analysis of wheat, oats, barley and rye are not necessarily applicable to prehistoric diets. These grains are the result of the advent of agriculture and listed in another table. They did not exist in their present form when evolution was perfecting the mammals of the world, so are not part of the discussion at the moment. They will be considered subsequently.

To assume that a root swelling of two million years ago is identical to a carrot of today is an uncertain reach. Nonetheless, such dot connecting is all we have, and not all that illogical, as we'll see. While any one food listed in the table may not be an ideal representation of what that food assayed in prehistoric times, the greater probability is that the table as a whole is appropriate for the conclusions drawn from it. The category of tender shoots contains the modern day analysis of celery and asparagus, neither of which may have existed two million years ago. Well, asparagus must have. It just looks prehistoric. Nonetheless, it is a fair assumption that tender shoots of prehistoric times were high in water, like these plants, and most probably similar in fiber and carbohydrate.

Table 7 (Abbreviated) Composition, g/100g (%) of food as found and eaten in the wild See Appendix page 178 for full table.

Food	Water	Protein	Fat	Fiber	Ash	Starch+Sugar (no fiber)
Spinach	91.4	2.9	0.4	2.2	1.72	0.4
Asparagus	93.2	2.2	0.6	2.1	0.58	1.9
Almonds	4.7	21.2	49.4	12.2	2.99	4.6
Pecans	3.5	9.1	72.0	9.6	1.49	4.4
Flax	6.7	18.3	42.2	27.3	3.72	1.5
Sesame	4.7	17.7	49.7	11.8	4.45	0.3
Blackberry	81.5	1.4	0.5	5.3	0.37	4.9
Peanut	6.5	25.8	49.2	8.5	2.33	4.0
Carrot	88.3	0.9	0.2	3.0	0.97	6.2

Table 7 (continued)

Food	Water	Protein	Fat	Fiber	Ash	Starch+Sugar (no fiber)
Potato	78.6	2.1	0.1	1.3	1.13	16.5
Apple	85.6	0.3	0.2	2.4	0.19	10.4
Tangerine	85.7	0.8	0.3	1.8	0.38	10.4
Squash	86.4	1.0	0.1	2.0	0.8	2.2
Fig	79.1	0.7	0.3	2.9	0.7	16.3
Venison	71.2	21.8	7.1	0	0.9	1.0
Chicken	75.8	19.6	3.9	0	1.0	0.5
Catfish	80.4	16.4	2.8	0	1.0	0.4
Snail	79.2	16.1	1.4	0	1.3	0.1

The fat content of fish, shellfish, insects and mammals, large and small, can cover a wide range. This should not surprise us, as we can look around us and see people of widely differing degrees of fat and thin. Nature intended that fat stores be adjustable, so depending on time of year and recent feeding luck, a given creature's fat content may be high or low. However, you will note that carbohydrate in these live foods is very low, and consistently so. As a matter of fact, when you review the entire list of foods in Table 7, very few are high in total carbohydrate, and even fewer are high in soluble carbohydrate, (total carbohydrate minus fiber). Sugar is very low in most foods, with dates (66 percent), apples (10 percent), and grapes (16 percent) conspicuous and rare exceptions.

This is one of the main points of this book. If a mammal ate 3.5 ounces (100 grams) of anything on this list, with only one or two exceptions, discussed below, they would eat very little soluble carbohydrate. Soluble carbohydrate is not the same as total carbohydrate. For raising blood sugar, starch is every bit the bad actor as sugar. So soluble carbohydrate is the term for what we are concerned about. Soluble carbohydrate is total carbohydrate minus fiber, basically starch plus sugar. This distinction is essential because what we are concerned with are foods that fit the enzymatic machinery of mammals, those that are an ill fit, and knowing the difference. Foods high in soluble carbohydrate, if a high percentage of the diet over time, are a bad fit for mammalian survival equipment. There just was never any great amount of sugar or soluble carbohydrate encountered by evolving mammals. Modern man changed that.

Soluble carbohydrate tends to raise blood sugar, and elicit the release of insulin. Fiber is too slowly digested, if at all, to affect any rapid increase in blood glucose. Therefore, it is fair when looking over Table 7 (in the Appendix format), to subtract the fiber value from the total carbohydrate value before ranking a food for its effect on blood sugar.

For example, flax seed is 28.9 percent total carbohydrate (fiber plus starch and sugar). But it is also 27.3 percent fiber, which is not rapidly available carbohydrate. When the fiber of flax is subtracted from the total carbohydrate, little remains. Acorns are reported as being high in total carbohydrate, but the known primitive peoples that based their diet on acorns are of more recent times, and had access to cooking methods for acorns. Acorns are quite bitter to the taste, due to tannic acid, which cooking addresses. Ancient mammals did no cooking as we know, so it leaves to speculation how many acorns were eaten in bygone days. Admittedly, hunger is quite given to expedience, and no doubt bitter, non-poisonous foods were eaten.

On occasion I have encountered coyote feces in late fall that were almost exclusively composed of the digesta of juniper berries (seed hulls, skin, stems). Juniper berries, used to make gin, smell strongly of turpentine or pine resin, and it was hard to imagine the hunger that drove anything to make a meal of them. One day I had to indulge my curiosity and ate a few juniper berries. They certainly had a turpentine flavor, but much to my surprise, the even stronger taste was sweet, which most likely meant nutrition from carbohydrate. And of course this made sense as I thought about it, for the first step in the production of any alcoholic beverage is fermentation, which requires sugar for the bacteria.

The main conclusion supported by Table 7 is that the primordial diet, at best, included small amounts of sugar and soluble carbohydrate no matter what food is considered. Potatoes and sweet potatoes are modern inventions, so to speak, meaning they were identified and genetically selected in the past 10,000 years. The same argument could be made for the grape.

According to the table, chestnuts, safflower seeds and cashews are the foods highest in carbohydrate, with 45, 34 and 30 grams, respectively, per 100 grams of food eaten. As pointed out below, these are not very high compared to many modern animal diet ingredients. These few high exceptions from nature's array would still be lower than any dry pet food or horse grain.

THE DRAWBACK OF DRY PET FOODS: EXCESS SOLUBLE CARBOHYDRATE

Table 8 lists the grains that have been the backbone of the agricultural revolution, started 10,000 years ago. These are also the grains that are the major component of dry dog and cat food, and horse grain. "Grain Free" is a descriptor for pet food intended to mean no corn, soy, wheat, barley or oats. This is the epitome of false security and I don't know who to criticize more loudly, the consumer that buys it or the marketer who pushes it. First of all, the problem is not grain, it is soluble carbohydrate, and the absence of specific grains does nothing to lessen the problem.

(I know there are those who condemn corn specifically, and its vast monoculture may indeed predispose some deficiency in its nutrient makeup. I assure you this is minor compared to the problem of excess starch.) The starch needed for the manufacturing process is obtained in other ways, such as potatoes, rice or peas.

Table 8 *Composition, g/100g (in other words, percent) of major grains as eaten Calcium (Ca) and phosphorus (P) are mg/100g.*

Food	Water	Protein	Fat	Ash	All Carbs	Fiber	Sugar	Starch	Ca	P
Wild rice	7.67	14.7	1.08	1.53	74.9	6.2	2.50	66.2	21	433
Brown rice	10.37	7.94	2.92	1.53	77.2	3.5	0.85	72.9	23	333
Wheat, soft	10.42	10.69	1.99	1.54	75.4	12.7	0.41	62.2	34	402
Wheat, hard	13.10	12.61	1.54	1.57	71.2	12.2	0.64	58.3	29	288
Corn, yellow	10.37	9.42	4.74	1.24	74.3	7.3	0.64	66.3	7	210
Barley, pearl	10.09	9.91	1.16	1.11	77.7	15.6	0.60	61.3	29	221
Oats	10.84	13.15	6.52	1.77	74.0	10.1	0.99	55.6	52	410
Average	11.21	74.0	63.3	1.47	75.0	9.6	0.94	63.0	28	328

Adapted from the USDA food data base at: www.nat.usda/fnic/foodcomp/search.

It is readily seen when pondering the total carbohydrate column of Table 8 that any one of these grains is a far greater source of carbohydrate than even the highest food on the list in Table 7. To complete the story of this central concept, consider the dry pet foods listed in Table 1. Here you will see that carbohydrate is high. Certainly higher than anyone's (person or animal) primordial ancestor ever ate. The average soluble carbohydrate of the dog foods listed in Table 1 is 41 percent. The average soluble carbohydrate of all the foods listed in Table 7 is 7.81 percent. This includes dates, at 66 percent, but does not include honey, at 82 percent. The typical dry dog food is over five times the level of soluble carbohydrate found in the primordial diet mammals have eaten from the beginning of their evolution. The analytical lab Dairyone Labs in Ithaca, New York, makes its results (without manufacturers' names) available to the public. On hundreds of samples of dry dog food, soluble carbohydrate averaged 39 percent. This disproportion is even more egregious for cats, as we'll see later.

So here we come to the fundamental point: not only is the modern dry diet higher in soluble carbohydrate than anything animals ever ate throughout evolution, but also the animal's biological machinery was perfected to eke out a survival in a world with near constant lack of soluble carbohydrate. This exquisite, designer perfect biological machinery is at a loss to deal very effectively with constant, excess soluble carbohydrate. The central problem is that a system designed and perfected to capture the rare blood sugar spike is now confronted with constant blood sugar spikes due to excess soluble carbohydrate.

As an analogy, imagine eyesight perfected by four billion years of evolution to operate in a world of starlight and twilight, suddenly asked to function in brilliant sunlight. Evolution would have to scramble to find a solution, and it would, but not before many went blind. And evolution will continue to perfect the fit of mammals to the new tidal wave of starch and sugar, but progress will be slow, because obesity and diabetes kill, but not soon enough to prevent reproduction and the same genes getting into offspring.

It is old news that excess carbohydrate is a component of obesity. Some clear thinking professionals have been saying this for years now. The late Dr. Atkins with his diet proposing unrestricted protein and fat is one of the more well-known proponents. Dr. Barry Sears, with his Zone Diet is perhaps the best informed technically of the diet gurus, and he, too, advocates the importance of a proper balance as to source of calories. But the consuming public still insists on buying products that advertise low fat. Or if you prefer, you can say product marketers still push products low in fat as the path to the land of the lean and trim. But the reason they do is because people buy products advertised this way.

Fat is not the problem. Fat consumption in the US has been going down in recent decades, along with beef consumption, but the obesity problem is getting worse. Why would the Atkins diet work (meaning in this case, lead to weight loss) if it permits all the fat you want and you still lose weight? Understand that the Atkins Diet in its extreme is a weight loss program, not a diet forever. They would be quick to point out, for example, that an athlete in training needs some carbohydrate (thereby echoing the teachings of Dr. Sears), and if at ideal weight, all need some.

It is recognized that the obesity calamity we are in, for pets and people, is a collision of several factors, among them lack of portion control and lack of exercise. But the consuming public of the western world is ill informed. This point was recently brought home to me when I was in the Middle East in Abu Dhabi. I saw a delivery truck with an advertisement (in English) that touted a diet bar that was low in carbohydrate, not fat. From this it would appear that in the Middle East they get it.

In the U.S., any supermarket offers untold dozens of products that brag on the label of being low in fat. "Fat reduced 50%" proclaims the label in bold print. The fine print, if any exists, reveals the fat was reduced from two percent of the total product contents to one percent. Yeah, that is correctly a 50 percent reduction.

Whether the fat reduction is large or small, when the percent of fat is reduced in a product, something has to replace it, and protein costs too much. Low fat usually means higher soluble carbohydrate, and a non-solution to obesity. It perplexed me greatly recently when I encountered a single serving coffee creamer labeled as "fat free" Half and Half. Ignoring the arcane food labeling laws that permit this oxymoron, how could it be Half and Half, a source of cream in any consumer's mind, and fat free? Regardless, the only way to lower fat is to add carbohydrate (protein would work too, but is too expensive).

The duped public, guided by government policy since the 1950s to avoid fat, increased sugar intake by default. In 1800, the annual per capita consumption of refined sugar in the US was essentially zero. In 1980, it was 124 pounds a year and by 1994 it was 150 pounds (See Figure 10). Today, it approaches one half pound of sugar per day.

If fat is the culprit, why when fat intake declines, and sugar increases, do we get fatter? Could it be that soluble carbohydrate is the greater problem?

Consider this additional supporting evidence. Archeologists have long known that people's health deteriorated with the advent of agriculture, meaning the domestication of cereal crops. In the 1930s, Weston Price reported on the dental and overall health of 11 different societies around the world. He studied these 11 ethnic groups because he found some of them living in a primitive, isolated group, and others of them living in a modernized or westernized group. Thus the ancestry and genetics were the same while the environment was different. In all cases, modernization of a people meant poor dental health and overall decline in fitness.

Gary Taubes in his book *Good Calories, Bad Calories*, gave special acknowledgement to Price's work. Kathleen Gordon of the Anthropology Department of the National Museum of Natural History in Washington wrote in 1987, "Nutritional deficiencies, which appear to have been rare in Paleolithic populations, have been common since the adoption of agriculture. Some have been particularly associated with the adoption of corn-based diets in the New World."

Arthur Keen of the Anthropology Department at the University of Massachusetts wrote in 1985, "The assumption that hunters and gatherers will satisfy their basic nutritional requirements is supported by empirical evidence that shows that hunters and gatherers subsisting on a traditional diet rarely suffer from any form of malnutrition or from nutritionally related diseases. When problems do develop, they are *due more to insufficient food supply* than to improper dietary scheduling." (Italics mine). Keen cites eight scholarly articles that he uses to support his point. The male skeletal remains of hunter-gatherers found in Greece and Turkey that date from the end of the ice age averaged 5' 9". After a few centuries of the agricultural revolution, in 3000 BC, they had shrunk to an average of 5' 3".

What is a traditional diet of a hunter-gatherer society? After all, it is just this diet in the few such groups extant today that everyone points to as being the representative model of bygone human diets. One must admit that the !Kung San of the Kalahari, or the Inuit of the Arctic do not cultivate grains, frequent restaurants or shop in grocery stores, and at least to this extent are far closer to a primordial diet than the rest of us.

Working with data adapted from others, Molnar divided subsistence food gatherers into foragers or pastoralists. Pastoralists husband at least some domesticated herbivores, while foragers subsist without domesticating any animals. They reported foragers obtain 85 percent of their calories from plants, 12 percent from meat, one percent from milk and two percent from meal. Pastoralists obtain 65 percent of their daily calories from plants, 11 percent from meat, 17 percent from milk and seven percent from meal. Average daily caloric intake for foragers was 2,100, peaking in April at 3,114. For pastoralists, daily intake averaged 2,314 calories, highest in May at 3,573. The additional 300 calories a day enjoyed by pastoralists would send a people into a famine with greater survival chances, and may be a factor in the rapid spread of the lactase persistence gene that enables adults to consume milk.

It is tempting to conclude, based on these figures, that this makes it obvious why the western world is fat, as we consume far more calories. Probably true, but keep in mind that these numbers are for smaller people, and all members of the group, which includes women and children. Remember, too, that in the southern hemisphere, April and May are the fall time of year. But 65 to 85 percent of the calories from plants is a useful number for insight. As seen in Table 7, a plant based diet provides very little soluble carbohydrate. Just as evident from Table 7 is that very little else available to a prehistoric forager provided much soluble carbohydrate. It didn't matter if you were a man, a dog or a cat, or ate only plants or only animals.

When speaking of hunter-gatherers, the concept of a "thrifty gene" alluded to in the introduction, was first suggested by Neel in 1962 and is succinctly reviewed by Stinson. This idea is accepted these days to mean that a beneficial trait, specifically the ability to thrive on hunter-gatherer fare is made harmful by the changed environment of modern times. The major evidence offered to substantiate this theory is the abnormally high incidence of adult-onset diabetes seen in hunter-gatherers thrust into modern society in the last half of the 20th century. Besides the Pima Indians of the American Southwest, the problem is found also in westernized Polynesians, Aboriginal Australians and the Nauru of Micronesia. I would add the tribe of all modern Americans and their animals.

We need to back the camera lens away from the map and get a broader view of the scene. It occurs to me that if pre-diabetes is an indication of the thrifty gene, then we all have the thrifty gene. And indeed, this is exactly what I suggest; that we have all inherited an exquisite ability to thrive on meager food intake, and a woeful ability to deal with constant excess soluble carbohydrate.

While conceding a problem with modern diets, other professional archeologists have implicated diet components other than carbohydrate. For example, Eaton and Konner compared modern day diets to pre-agricultural hunter-gatherer diets (using as a model contemporary hunter-gatherer societies) and stated that modern diets are lower in protein, fiber, vitamin C and calcium, and higher in fat and sodium. They leave out any mention of carbohydrate. In so doing they fall in with the attitude prevalent since the 1950s that fat is the culprit in our diets. When these researchers omit any mention of excess soluble carbohydrate, they overlook an important factor. Are we to assume that the lowered protein and fiber of modern diets were replaced solely by increased fat? As we've noted, an important and significant difference between our modern diet and primordial hunter-gatherers is our higher level of soluble carbohydrate.

Perhaps it does not seem a reasonable hypothesis to you that mammals are poorly equipped to process excess calories from carbohydrate. If different words are used to say the same thing, there is overwhelming evidence of its validity. What if we stated the hypothesis (that constant excess soluble carbohydrates are detrimental) instead as caloric restriction allows longer life? Every time caloric restriction was investigated, regardless of species, the animals lived longer compared to controls fed more calories. This held true if the experimental creature was yeast, roundworms, monkeys, mice and now dogs.

In a well-designed study, Purina (Nestle) undertook a much needed experiment using Labrador dogs for their entire lives. The study lasted 15 years. In this study, caloric restriction led to an average of two years longer life. In a follow-on study using urine saved from these dogs it was shown that one effect of the diet restriction was lower metabolic rate.

There is another way of looking at the same concept, that constant excess dietary calories are an enigma for nature. It is well established that when sick with a fever, an animal will reduce food intake. Researchers found when caloric intake was forced back to normal in chickens that had decreased their food intake due to sickness, the level of mortality went up significantly. This is further evidence that evolutionary machinery never perfected much capacity for dealing with excess calories.

Little else better highlights the main theme of this book than a 2007 article in the journal *Nutrition Reviews* by Levenson and Rich. In this study of caloric restriction, they mention several papers that show even the brain itself responds to lower calories with fewer age-related declines in neurogenesis in older animals.

SUMMARY

Mammals have a highly perfected system for capturing any and all spikes in blood sugar and saving this energy as stored fat. This ability is the result of billions of years of Darwinian adaptation to a world that provided no ongoing excess of carbo-hydrate calories. Within the last few moments of the geological day, through plant domestication, creative hominids have arranged for constant excess calories from soluble carbohydrates. Man's overuse of carbohydrate calories has spilled over into animal foods that often, especially in the dry form, are too high in soluble carbo-hydrate. A bag of potato chips and a Coke will get you to the next day just fine, in keeping with nature's design and exquisite adaptability. But we all know this is not a proper diet. A lifetime of eating excess soluble carbohydrates is a lifetime that is shorter than it needs to be.

Large breed dogs are the most costly to feed and hence more likely to be on dry diets, which cost the least. Thus large breeds are the most compromised by excess calories from soluble carbohydrates and possibly this is a factor in their shorter lifespan compared to smaller breeds. Great Danes die essentially of old age at the age of eight, and we shrug and say it comes with the breed. Perhaps a short life is part of the bargain when you bring home a Dane puppy, but eight years? Maybe a life with less endocrine abuse would last longer.

Dr. Ian Billinghurst, author of the acclaimed book *Give Your Dog a Bone*, written in Australia, has lectured all over the world, including my living room, that diets that are more natural are better for health and longevity. He bases this point of view on his patients over the decades that consumed commercial diets (urban) and experi-enced ill health, and those that ate natural diets (rural, farm) and enjoyed longer, healthier lives.

An intriguing report about early Arctic explorers would add credence to those advo-cating a raw or natural diet. Historically, Europeans long at sea or in the Arctic suf-fered the vitamin C deficiency of scurvy, while native people living in the same area did not. Eating the native diet, cooked in the European style, did not prevent the disease, until it was observed that Inuit ate only fresh or lightly cooked meat. There is adequate vitamin C in raw meat to sustain health, but harsh cooking destroys it. While Dr. Billinghurst makes good points, not all commercial diets are bad, and not all natural diets are good.

Next we will examine the flexibility evolution built into mammalian metabolism to enable survival in the face of intermittent or uncertain nourishment.

REFERENCES

Stromatolites, primordial cells… Fortey R. 1997. Life. A Natural history of the first four billion years of life on earth. Vintage Books ed. Random House, Inc. New York.

3000 year old barley… Shewry PR, Kirkman MA, Burgess SR, et al. 1982. Comparison of the amino acid composition of old and recent barley grain. New Phytologist. 90:455-466.

the rat always selects… Hrupka, BJ, M Lin, DW Gertzen, QR Rogers. 1997. Small changes in the essential amino acid content alter diet selection in amino acid-deficient rats. J. Nutr. 127:777-784.

Arsenic needed by humans… Nielsen FH. 2001. Boron, manganese, molybdenum and other trace elements. In: Present Knowledge in Nutrition, 8th ed. ILIS Press. Wash. DC. Page 392.

Vitamin C terminal step turned off… Lucock M. 2007. Molecular Nutrition and Genomics. Nutrition and the Ascent of Humankind. John Wiley and Sons, Inc. Hoboken, NJ. pg 60.

Sugar considered a medicine… Brothwell D, Brothwell M. 1998. Food in Antiquity. A survey of the diet of early peoples. Johns Hopkins Paperback edition. Johns Hopkins University press. Baltimore. Page 80.

Bees 100 million years old… Salem-News.com. 2006. http://www.salemnews.com/articles/october262006/old_bee_102606.php

The analytical lab in New York… Dairyone Lab. Itaca, New York. http://www.dairyone.com/Forage/FeedComp/Main_GatResults.asp.

Zone diets of Dr. Barry Sears… Sears B. 2002. The Omega Rx Zone. The miracle of the new high-dose fish oil. Reagan Books, Harper Collier Publishers Inc. New York. 10022.

Obesity problem is getting worse… Doyle R. 2006. Sizing Up: Roots of obesity epidemic lie in the mid-20th century. Scientific American (Feb.) Page 32.

Annual per capita consumption of sugar… Steward HL, Bethea MC, Andews SS, Balart LA. 1998. Sugarbuster!™ Cut sugar to trim fat. Ballantine Publishing Group. New York. Page 19.

Overall decline in fitness… Price, Weston. 1945. Nutrition and physical degeneration. A comparison of primitive and modern diets and their effects. Price-Pottenger Foundation. Santa Monica, Ca 90403

book Good Calories Bad Calories… Taubes, Gary. 2007. Good calories, bad calories. Challenging the conventional wisdom on diet, weight control and disease. Knopf. New York. Price, pg 575: Vit C, pg 456.

Nutritional deficiencies rare… Gordon KD. 1987. Evolutionary Perspectives on Human Diet. In: Nutritional Anthropology. Francis E. Johnson, Ed. Alan R. Liss, Inc. New York. Page 29.

Corn based diets in the new world...Gordon KD. 1987. Evolutionary Perspective on Human Diet. In: Nutritional Anthropology. F. E. Johnson, Ed. Alan R Liss, Inc. New York. Page 29.

Due more to insufficient food supply... Keen AS. 1985. Nutrition and Economy: Models for the Study of Prehistoric Diet. In: The analysis of Prehistoric Diets. Robert Gilbert and James Mielke, eds. Academic Press, Inc. New York. Page 158.

After a few centuries of agricultural revolution... Diamond, J. 1987. The worst mistake in the history of the human race. Discover 8 (no 5): 64-66.

85% of their calories from plants... Molnar S, Molnar IM. 2000. Environmental Change and Human Survival. Some Dimensions of Human Ecology. Prentice Hall. Upper Saddle River, NJ. Page 178.

Lactase persistence gene... Check E. 2006. How Africa Learned to Love the Cow. Nature, Vol. 444, Dec 21/28. Page 994.

Thrifty gene first mentioned... Neel JV. 1962. Diabetes Mellitus: A "thrifty" genotype rendered detrimental by "progress." Am. J. Hum. Genet. 14:353-362.

Thrifty gene reviewed... Stinson S. 1992. Nutritional adaptation. Annu. Rev. Anthropol. 21:143-170.

Compared modern diets... Eaton SB, Konner M. 1985. Paleolithic Nutrition. A consideration of its natural and current implications. New England Journal of Med. 312:283-289. Cited by KD Gordon (ref #30), page 30.

Caloric restriction... Levenson CW, Rich NJ. 2007. Eat less, live longer? New insights into the role of caloric restriction in the brain. Nutr. Rev. 65:412-415.

Much needed experiment... Kealy R., D.F. Lawler, J. M. Ballam, S.L. Mantz, D.N. Biery, E.H. Greeley, G. Lust, M. Segre, G.K. Smith, H. D. Stowe. 2002. Effect of diet restriction on life span and age-related changes in dogs. J. Am. Vet. Med. Assoc. 220:1315-1320.

Urine saved from dogs... Wang Y, Lawler D, Larson B, et al. 2007. Metabolic investigation of aging and caloric restriction in life-long dog study. J. Proteome Res., 6 (5):1846-1854. dio: 10.1021/pr060685n.

Mortality went up... Murray MJ, Murray AB. 1979. Anorexia of infection as a mechanism of host defence. Am. J. Clin. Nutr. 32:593-596.

Billinghurst... Billinghurst I. 1993. Give your dog a bone. The practical commonsense way to feed dogs for a long healthy life. Billinghurst Publ. P.O. Box WO64 Bathurst, N.S.W. Australia.

Adequate Vitamin C in raw meat... Taubes, Gary. 2007. Good calories, bad calories. Challenging the conventional wisdom on diet, weight control and disease. Knopf. New York. Price, pg 575: Vit C, pg 456.

4

ADAPTABILITY PERFECTED BY LACK
(BILLIONS OF YEARS OF DEALING WITH LACK
MADE MAMMALS GOOD AT IT)

As a biological entity, mammals have an exact and precise set of enzymes, hormones, and all attendant molecular machinery that was evolved by Darwinian selection. By the dawn of upright man, about four million years ago, this biochemistry was within two percent of today's precision. One could argue that mammals are the ultimate designer product, having their gene pool skillfully crafted and engineered to interface with their environment with maximum efficiency. The two irreducible pillars of existence for any species are first, survival and second, reproduction. The only purpose of one is to allow the other. Propelling genes forward, in combination with survival tricks in the face of scarcity, has proven immensely successful. Little short of a meteor from outer space has challenged the species survival system operating today.

INTO THE NEXT GENERATION

An all-powerful imperative of a species is to get its genes into the next generation. Plan A blaring away seasonally, if not daily in the activity of any creature, is find a mate, procreate. It seems the only Plan B is "See Plan A." Nature's approach is straightforward and simply this: It doesn't matter if full genetic expression is not realized in every specimen, if the species successfully reproduces another generation with equal adaptability and potential. Nature's attitude is indifferent and unencumbered with any preoccupation of modern day issues about ethics or quality of life. If it can be guaranteed there will always be seeds, soil quality can be disregarded. This of course places tremendous emphasis on the "if" part of nature's plan. The premise of this chapter, and one central to the entire story, is that nature has many maneuvers to enable species survival in the face of all sorts of trouble, or soil types if you will, but these finally are only to enable the lone strategy, that being to get the genes into the next generation.

Consider the powerful and irresistible drive to reproduce. To begin, imagine the routine daily existence of early man. At times it was a constant search for food, if water was sufficient. And this search was not necessarily in a tropical paradise. It often entailed a full day's effort, going from one berry bush to another, to a few tender shoots of grass to an insect or two. On occasion, it may have included a team effort to ensnare a small mammal or fish. It also quite often entailed escaping from a larger mammal intent on collecting a meal for itself. Vigilance for one's self and tribe mates, with attendant energy costs, was a constant price paid by all and if forsaken, followed swiftly by dire consequences. At the end of the day, the little band probably climbed into trees for increased safety and a fitful rest, sometimes with raging hunger after an unsuccessful day of foraging.

Early on, nature realized there had to be a strong urge to reproduce. It had to be an urge that routinely subjugated all other feelings and conditions like pain, fatigue, hunger, sunburn, mosquitoes, heat, cold and (almost certainly) headache. Modern morals are a flea in front of an avalanche. The reason guys thinks about sex every 20 minutes is because all those who thought about it every 25 minutes became extinct. This is a classic example of evolution at its best, like it or not. This is the effect of testosterone. It does the job it was invented for just fine. The only catch is that the world it was invented for no longer exists for mankind, or his companion animals.

To blame all our urges on testosterone is of course too simplistic and rudely short-changes the inspiring beauty of the biochemistry of reproduction. Estrogen and dozens of other male and female hormones, pheromones, releasing factors, receptors and chemical messengers also play a big role in the reproductive synchrony for humans as well as animals. Regardless, the imperative to reproduce is powerful by design. A design that was an absolutely essential and successful solution, in a time long ago.

Experts believe there has been a mass extinction five times since mother earth began, with the last, a meteor hitting Yucatan 65 million years ago, obliterating not only all dinosaurs, but also 95 percent of all known life. Imagine how crucial the sex drive in the surviving five percent of creatures. For eons mankind has grown and perfected and multiplied, filling the earth to the point of fouling his own nest (many would say). One might think nature would give us a break and ease up on the sex urge part of our existence[1].

Keep in mind that the current state of affairs, meaning seven billion people, has come to pass in the last few seconds of a geological day. Figuratively speaking, nature is not influenced in the least by how many miles mankind has driven without an accident. From nature's perspective, man's recent proliferation is irrelevant in the grand scheme, and there will be no altering of the reproductive imperative. This seat belt of mammalian survival remains standard issue, factory installed, in each unit.

---

[1]*In fact it is known in mice that crowding lowers reproduction.*

DEALING WITH LACK

Regarding mammals and their daily survival, one major assignment of all the thousands of enzyme systems faithfully transferred forward by genes is to deal with lack or insufficiency: in the first place, lack of a basic nutrient, such as protein or copper, and in the second place, lack of subsequent or secondary products, such as amino acids or copper dependent enzymes. We can endure the lack of certain nutrients for months, and in some instances, years. Everyone has skipped a meal now and then, many fast for days on a voluntary basis, and the annals of history are full of tales of survival for weeks or months on the most meager of rations. What is even more intriguing, the emaciation of months of starvation in adults is usually repaired without a trace in a relatively short time. Figure 9 shows an adult Doberman rescued by animal control as he lay near death from starvation, weighing 35 lbs. With proper care, he went on to live a long normal life.

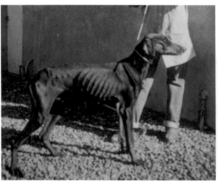

Figure 9 *Adult Doberman weighing 35 lbs. at rescue went on to live 10 more years.*

Admittedly, malnutrition of sub adults can cause irreparable harm, but even in the young, the capacity for compensatory hypertrophy (extra growth to make up for poor earlier growth) can in many cases essentially reverse the ill effects of stunted growth. *For more on this Doberman, see End Notes page 165.*

The average male in London in 1833 was 5' 3" and the school desks of prewar Japanese children were too small for subsequent generations of the same age. The wall niches used for beds 400 years ago at Fort Augustine, Florida, are too small for contemporary man. Northern European Bronze age homes, preserved for our modern day edification, are surprisingly small. These observations point out that the suboptimal nutrition and environment of the past did little to prevent these people from propagating. They dealt with the lack of nutrition at hand while passing on to their descendants a genetic package fully capable of enabling larger size if and when better nutrition became available. Mammals can accommodate a temporary deficiency of anything.

For higher mammals' survival, numerous tactics are in place to keep the species functioning sufficiently to allow reproduction. To begin with, all mammals have two of nearly everything; ears, nostrils, eyes, lungs, kidneys and brain hemispheres, to name a few. Severed arteries and veins clot, broken bones knit; if knocked unconscious, breathing continues. The less eaten, the more of it is digested. Body fat reserves are mobilized during times of low energy intake.

One of the most eloquent illustrations of a species survival tactic is seen in pregnancy. During mild starvation, a pregnant mother's peripheral tissues grow less sensitive to insulin. Insulin promotes blood glucose into the cells. The rationale in this case is to protect the next generation by directing the mother's limited glucose supply to the fetus at the expense of the mother's outlying and non- critical tissues. The gamble is that this is a price worth paying on a temporary basis, as it improves the chances of an offspring in an otherwise risky lot. However, if the starvation becomes severe, the peripheral tissues return to their normal sensitivity to insulin. This usually ends pregnancy, which is integral to the plan, as the mother thereby needs less food and has a better chance of outlasting the famine, to become a mother later in better times.

Consider this adaptation to lack in a bit more detail. What happens if the diet doesn't provide enough vitamin A? No problem. The liver has stored enough for months or even years in some cases. Polar bears will eat an entire Ring seal, except for the liver, so high in vitamin A that it is toxic. The seal's liver vitamin A was derived from all the fish it ate. At the cellular level, the breakdown of energy compounds most efficiently happens in the presence of oxygen (from air in the lungs). But there is also a way that cells derive energy from the same compounds if there is no oxygen.

The first, using oxygen, is called aerobic glycolysis, the other is called anaerobic glycolysis. Anaerobic glycolysis is much less efficient, but it does permit muscle activity in the absence of oxygen. And these energy compounds? They are not just glucose: amino acids from protein digestion can be converted to glucose. As a matter of fact, some amino acids are so readily converted to glucose that they are called glucogenic amino acids.

A mammal's stored fat is the first reserve employed to shore up lack of energy that has persisted for more than a few days. Some people are literally carrying around a half year's supply of calories. A pound of fat has nine calories per gram, or 4,086 calories. If overweight by 100 pounds, it represents 408,600 calories. With a daily need of 1,800 calories, this is over 200 days' worth. There exists in all species an unfailing biochemical pathway to extract energy – the most critical nutrient – from fat, protein or carbohydrate. For fiber, plant eaters, omnivores and carnivores have the symbiotic arrangement with bacteria that ferment fiber into propionate, which the liver converts to glucose. As mentioned in the Chapter 2 discussino of fiber, it is estimated that up to half of a pig's maintenance energy needs can be met by this hindgut fermentation.

A classic example of a backup system is calcium. If dietary calcium is lacking and blood levels are low, bone is dissolved to restore blood levels. If sodium is scarce, the kidney can virtually shut down sodium excretion. If zinc is deficient, uptake from the diet is increased.

What is going on here? How can we survive for days without food, for weeks with nearly none, and for months with only morsels? For hundreds of millions of years, mammals have benefited on a daily basis from the survival equipment at their disposal, and primordial man was no exception. Mammals have always had the ability to deal with lack, insufficiency, absence and shortage, including, or maybe even especially, our companion animals. It is an absolutely wondrous ability, representing probably the most crucial adaptation for keeping the individual upright and going forward. There is a solution or backup for anything that is liable to become scarce, including any enzyme of metabolism. Every enzyme so far discovered and studied catalyzes more than one reaction. An enzyme may catalyze one specific reaction better than any other enzyme, but it also can speed other reactions.

Adaptations for lack of water were essential. When talking about the need for ongoing nourishment, demise by thirst is the most rapid and instant fate we can suffer (with the obvious exception of oxygen). Still, the human body can go for a time without water. The length of this privation is a function of temperature and activity, with exertion in the desert sun leading to a coma in a few days or even hours. But in a comfortable temperature and resting state, the coma of thirst could be several days in arriving. Most species can go about a week without water.

One of the techniques for dealing with a water shortage is what is called metabolic water. Metabolism of food produces water in the body, which can serve some of the body's needs for water. Up to half of urine volume can be from metabolic water – in other words, from food, not consumed liquids. In some species, this backup maneuver can assume front row status. The wallaroo in Australia, when living in caves, can go for long periods without water. In addition to using metabolic water, they are mostly nocturnal, spend the heat of the day in cool rock recesses, and browse early morning dew-moistened plants and tuberous roots. Most desert dwelling herbivores take advantage of this morning foraging, adapting to the survival rhythm of the local plants. Desert plants tend to draw water from the leaves in the heat of the sun, and return it to the leaves in the cool of the night. This effect is maximized at dawn. Cats, thought to have originated as a desert species, are adept at relying on the water content of their food, and drinking very little.

SUGAR

The widespread misunderstanding of sugar and the crescendo of grief in its wake compel an early appearance at our grand jury. The topic of sugar and starch could logically fit in the earlier section on chemical makeup of food (Chapter 2), or in the discussion about what was in the primordial diet (Chapter 3). Being a more recent factor, and mostly man made, it is discussed here.

Public health officials have long puzzled over the fact that obesity is more prevalent among the poor, those least able to afford fattening diets or life style. A full understanding of sugar and starch explains this paradox. Throughout evolution, oxygen could be depended on. Water could be scarce, but this lack was invariably slow in developing, allowing migration. Energy was a different matter. The species that perfected an ability to endure lack of energy intake was more successful.

Enter insulin, the hormone. A small, simple molecule produced in the beta cells of the pancreas, insulin is made of 51 amino acids in two chains. With only one or two amino acid changes, it is found in nearly all forms of life. Insulin from the humble codfish differs from human insulin only in that it has one more amino acid in the B chain. All mammalian species have insulin, as well as their own version of every other human hormone. In most cases, the molecular structure of these numerous hormones is nearly or exactly identical across species.

Insulin's function, among other things, is to get sugar from the blood into the cell. In fact, insulin is the only hormone that lowers blood sugar. Adrenalin, the corticoids, glucagon and growth hormone all raise blood sugar. There are eight known hormones that raise blood sugar, while only insulin lowers it. (The other four are vasopressin, melanocyte stimulating hormone, thyroid stimulating hormone and norepinephrine.) This is telling. From the viewpoint of the evolution of survival tricks, keeping blood sugar held up to the proper and necessary level would appear to have been a much larger concern than keeping blood sugar down to the proper level. And indeed, from the time our ancestors swung down from the trees, through the ensuing millions of years, keeping blood sugar held up to an essential minimum was critical.

Insulin was invented, so to speak, to capture the rare and precious spike in blood sugar, such as when honey or a lush patch of ripe fruit was encountered. Not much else in the list of food options caused a spike in blood sugar. Hence the very reason insulin was important. Elevated blood sugar was an infrequent bonanza. It was only on rare occasions that a creature had the luxury of elevated blood sugar, and a tireless sentry like insulin that captured this excess blood glucose was invaluable.

Many pets, both dogs and cats, are fed a dry, expanded kibble diet, which must be manufactured with at least a third or more starch. Because of this starch, following every meal of dry kibble diet there is a blood glucose spike, leading to an insulin surge, and insulin performing its tireless duty. The thing is, insulin was not invented to be called on several times a day.

But wait. There's more. Insulin's function is not just to move blood sugar into the cells. Its second and equally powerful role is to promote the conversion of blood sugar into fat and save it in body fat reserves, while simultaneously stopping breakdown and mobilization of storage fat. [This is crucial to understand. Please read the last sentence again.]

For this reason, it is not belaboring the obvious to say a fat individual is fat because they can't lose weight. If the diet is constantly spiking insulin, weight loss will be a struggle even with restricted intake.

There is a complementary other half to this story. Insulin operates in tandem with another hormone called glucagon. The role of glucagon is the opposite of insulin: to mobilize stores of energy, both liver glycogen and body fat reserves, and to keep blood glucose supported. Inasmuch as high blood sugar, and thus the need for insulin, was a relatively infrequent happening in the primordial world, and low blood sugar far more common, it was intended that glucagon predominate as the principle glucose regulating hormone. When glucagon is up, insulin is down, and vice versa. While this arrangement neatly stabilized blood glucose throughout the eons of evolution, today there is a ready availability of foods that spike blood sugar. Figure 10 shows the dramatic rise in per capita sugar consumption in the last 200 years.

It is one third pound a day! And this ignores starch, which is equally sinful. This leaves us having to constantly guard against excess blood glucose. If on the other hand we focused on keeping insulin at bay, glucagon will automatically predominate, a big help keeping body condition in line. For ourselves, and our pets, we should strive to keep to a minimum foods that spike insulin, which are those that raise blood glucose, which means starch and sugar. [For more on hormones, see end notes.]

Foods that cause blood sugar to rise quickly, resulting in insulin secretion (and thereby setting up obesity), are all carbohydrates. They vary in their potency for raising glucose, which is a reflection of the speed with which they dissolve in the gut milieu, are broken down by enzymes, are absorbed into the intestinal cell and enter the blood. Some sugars, such as sucrose on your kitchen table, quickly lead to elevated blood glucose.

Keep in mind that table sugar is a disaccharide, containing two sugar molecules, one of glucose and one of fructose, and it must be cleaved into one molecule of glucose and one molecule of fructose before it can alter blood levels of glucose. As we know, this happens quickly.

Figure 10 *Average sugar consumption per person in the United States*

Starches and glycogen are long chains of glucose, and depending on how rapidly they are digested, they too can raise blood glucose quickly. Speed of digestion and how quickly a given carbohydrate leads to elevated blood sugar can be influenced by numerous things. Cooking of starches increases their digestibility. The other components of the food can be a factor. Pioneers in this field observed that foods high in protein and fat tended to cause less blood glucose rise. Foods that release their glucose slowly, for whatever reason, will tend not to spike blood sugar, and therefore not to elicit insulin. The result, as described above, is that the hormone glucagon, insulin's opposite, stays elevated, leading to fat deposits being mobilized, which greatly helps keep a body trim.

The ability of a food to raise blood glucose is called its glycemic index. A listing of the glycemic index of 1,000 different foods is available to anyone. The listing of foods according to their glycemic index is quite a step forward in our understanding of nutrition. Even though this concept was first promoted more than 25 years ago, it is only recently receiving consideration in the U.S. Other countries early on grasped the utility of this idea and incorporated it into the nutrition dialogue.

Only a fraction of the 1,000 foods listed in the glycemic index are from U.S. research. Many are from Australia, Canada and other countries. Table 9 shows several common foods and their glycemic index. *For more about glycemic index see End Notes page 167, and the expanded Table 9 in the Appendix page 171.*

Table 9 *Glycemic Index (GI), and Glycemic Load (GL) of different foods.*[1] *(Abbreviated) More expanded form in the Appendix as Expanded Table 9.*

Food (number of studies)	GI	GL[2]
Glucose (11)	99	-
Fructose(6)	19	2
Low		
Hummus (chickpea dip)	6	0
Peanuts (3)	14	1
Milk, whole (5)	27	3
Cashews	22	3
Soybeans (2)	18	1
Medium		
Ice cream (high fat)	37	4
Honey (11)[3]	55	10
Spaghetti (70), foreign	44	21
Strawberries, fresh	40	1
Grapefruit	25	3
Grapes (2)	46	8
Sweet corn (2), USA	60	20
Oat bran	55	3
Peas (3), boiled	48	3
Carrots (4)	47	3
Whole grain bread	51	7
Coca Cola (2)	58	16
High		
Rice (13)	64	23
Potato (4)	85	26
Sweet potato	61	17

High		
French fries	75	22
Popcorn	72	8
Jelly beans	78	22
Rice Krispies (breakfast cereal)	82	22
Shredded Wheat (breakfast cereal)	83	17
White bread (USA)	70	10
Donut	76	17

[1]*Source: International Table of Glycemic Index and Glycemic Load Values 2002. Foster-Powell, K., S. Holt, and J. C. Brand-Miller. Am. J. Clin. Nutr. 2002; 765-756.*

[2]*Glycemic Load can be influenced by several things, such as test serving size, or fiber. For example, oat bran and sweet corn are nearly identical in GI, but quite different in GL. This is most probably due to the fiber content of oat bran.*

[3]*Honey was listed with a wide range of GI, from 35 to 87. Pure honey is listed at 58. The high level of fructose (GI=19) in honey may be part of the reason its GI is low for a high sugar food. Coca-Cola is high in fructose, thus deceptively low in GI.*

One can see from looking at the table that the spread is not as wide as one might have expected, with many foods clustering around 50. There are extremes, such as peanuts at 14, ice cream surprisingly low at 37, breakfast cereals at 82, and jelly beans at 78. It is quite easy in today's world of fast food and manufactured foods to inadvertently select a diet of high glycemic index foods. For one thing, sugar is included in countless manufactured foods. Alternatively, a hypothetical list of foods eaten by a health food proponent would present a much lower average.

In reality, the truest picture is gained by a little further consideration. Nutritionists refer to a concept called glycemic load, which is the glycemic index multiplied by the amount of sugar in a serving. A food may have some sucrose in it that quickly raises blood glucose, but if there is very little of this sugar, it may not be as offensive as a food with a lot more carbohydrate. Table 9 also shows glycemic load. This value tends to run from 0 to 30, and gives a more realistic picture of diet effect on eliciting insulin. While fruits can have a high glycemic index, their glycemic load is low due to the low amount of sugar per serving – they're all water.

A small steady inflow of a modest amount of sugar into the blood is not only harmless, but by design, it is essential. A food may provide a quickly digested sugar, but if there is only a small amount of this sugar, and the food is eaten in modest amounts, the blood sugar level does not necessarily exceed the threshold trigger level for insulin release, and insulin stays out of the picture.

An appreciation of this interplay of dietary carbohydrate and hormone response is important to a clear understanding of obesity and weight control. We must start with the unsettling consideration that decades of government diet advice may require rethinking. A low fat diet will only lead to grudging weight loss if it is high in soluble carbohydrate. One way to help organize all the rhetoric about diet and weight loss is to imagine a three legged stool (Figure 11) with each leg representing one of the three basic factors in weight loss. The first leg is exercise. Everyone gets it that exercise uses calories. The second leg is portion control. Here again, everyone gets it. The less you eat, the fewer calories consumed. The third leg is diet composition. Nobody gets this, including government dietary recommendations.

Figure 11 *The three basic parts to the weight loss discussion are exercise, portion control and diet composition. Everyone understands the first two. Nobody seems to get the third.*

It has been known for over a century that starch and sugar are fattening. In 1995 the *New York Times* best seller *Sugarbusters!* was released, to little avail. But the tipping point is at least closer. A recent scientific paper in the *Journal of the American Medical Association (JAMA)* clearly implicates added sugar in the American diet as correlated with cardiovascular disease and mortality. Finally, the medical profession may be coming to the party. Robert Lustig and colleagues of the University of California, San Francisco, published a paper in 2012 in the scientific journal *Nature* titled *Public Health: The toxic truth about sugar*. His lecture on YouTube has had 2.5 million hits. It seems this topic has finally moved more onto center stage in the popular media, with several newspapers running stories (e.g. *Wall Street Journal*, May 3-4, 2014: *Fat Reconsidered*) and release of the movie *Fed Up* produced by Katie Couric and Laurie David, producer of *Inconvenient Truth*. The *HuffPost Healthy Living* ran a story August 6, 2014 by Elizabeth Svoboda writing for *Men's Journal* headed *Is sugar the new tobacco?* Hopefully, those who for years have been hammering in vain on this confusion in the national nutrition dialogue (Dr. Atkins, Dr. Sears, Gary Taubes) can now look forward to vindication.

The paradox of the obese poor can now be explained. If shopping with meager funds to feed a family, the most food for the dollar is carbohydrate (thank you American behemoth Agribusiness), which as explained is the most fattening. For decades public officials told us, wrongly, that fat was the problem. It is not. Starch and sugar are the problem.

A search of the web will turn up a modest but growing list of trials looking at glycemic index in pets. The veterinary profession seems to be showing appropriate interest in examining the carbohydrate level of cat foods, as it is more intuitive that a carnivore such as the cat might not need a constant high carbohydrate intake. Such interest in the dog lags behind. A French trial used carefully controlled conditions to evaluate 20 different commercial wet and dry diets fed to dogs and found that the amount of starch consumed is the major determinant of the glucose response of healthy dogs; the higher the starch content of the diet, the higher the blood glucose increase. They also reported that the higher the dietary fat of the diet, the lower the blood glucose rise. Could it be that fat is not the villain, but that high carbohydrate may be a problem?

Glycemic index is not the last word in energy digestibility. It is just one more aid in understanding the science of nutrition. As mentioned, it was pointed out by Jenkins and coworkers in the first papers on this topic that foods high in fat and protein tend to be lower in glycemic index. Whole milk, which is one third protein and one third fat, is low (27) in glycemic index, and so, too, peanuts (13), which are 40 percent protein and 25 percent fat.

Another important point: There is not to be found on the list any beef, poultry, egg, fish, avocado, salad greens or cheese. These foods contain so little carbohydrate that it would be very difficult for a test volunteer to eat enough of them to consume the grams of carbohydrate called for by the international test protocol. For example, to get 50 grams of sugar from cheese, one would need to eat four pounds of cheese. This tells us a great deal about these foods. They are not involved in raising blood sugar, so they would promote elevated blood glucagon, and therefore body depot fat mobilization, meaning weight loss.

To summarize, animals are very well adapted to deal with temporary deficiencies of nutrients. The world they evolved in confronted them with constant intermittent shortage of one nutrient or another. At any given time, there was invariably a lack of something. The immutable discipline of Darwinian selection perfected a collection of survival tactics layered with contingency plans, redundancy and solutions for essentially any shortage. This constant lack gave rise to an eloquence of adaptability to lack. As a direct consequence, however, our pets are poorly adapted to deal with excess. There was never any selective pressure to promote a genotype that excelled on constant abundance of food, because there never was constant abundance of food. Remember: insulin saves blood sugar as body fat, and constant excess soluble carbohydrate activates insulin and can cause obesity. Over a lifetime, it leads to poor health, and thereby a shorter life span.

As mentioned in Chapter 3, it has been proven in numerous diverse species, including the dog, that caloric restriction in general, and not just from sugar, extends life significantly. Again, this supports the hypothesis that mammalian metabolism was shaped by evolution to accommodate deficiency, and is compromised by constant excess.

REFERENCES

obliterating not only all dinosaurs... Fortey R. Fossils: The key to the past. 2002. Smithsonian Institution Press, Washington DC, in association with the Natural History Museum, London. Page 181.

The average male in London... Solomons, NW, M Mazarieogo, KH Brown and K Klasing. 1993. The underprivileged, developing country child: Environment contamination and growth failure revisited. Nutr. Rev. 51:327-332.

peripheral tissue return to their sensitivity... Bell AW. 1995. Regulation of organic nutrient metabolism during transition from late pregnancy to early lactation. J. Anim. Sci. 73:2804-2819.

can go for long periods without water...Walker EP. 1975. Mammals of the World, Vol I. Third ed. John Hopkins University Press. Baltimore. Page 89.

relying on water content of their food...Kane, E., QR Rogers, JG Morris, PMB Leung. 1981. Feeding behavior of the cat fed laboratory and commercial diets. Nutr. Res. 1:499-507.

leading to an insulin surge... Nguyen P., H. Dumon, V. Biorge, E. Pouteau. 1998. Glycemic and insulinemic response after ingestion of commercial foods in healthy dogs: Influence of food composition. J. Nutr. 128:2654S-2658S.

Many researchers are pursuing this question... Friedman MI. 1998. Food partitioning and food intake. Am. J. Clin. Nutr. 67:513S-518S....and, Langhans W. 1995. Role of the liver in the metabolic control of eating: What we know and what we do not know. Neuroscience and Biobehavioral Rev. 20:145-153...and, Konturek PC, Konturek JW, Czensnikiewicz-Gruzik M, et. al. 2005. Neuro-hormonal control of food intake: Basic mechanisms and clinical implications. J. Phys. Pharm. 56(Suppl 6):5-25...and, Morton GJ, Cummings DE, Baskin DG, et al. 2006. Central nervous system control of food intake and body weight. Nature. 443: 289-295. doi:10.1038/nature05026.

Pioneers in this field... Jenkins DJA, Wolever TMS, Taylor RH, et al. 1981. Glycemic index of foods: a physiological basis for carbohydrate exchange. Am. J. Clin. Nutr. 34:362-366.

Glycemic index of 1000 foods... Foster-Powell K, Holt SHA, Brand-Miller JC. International table of glycemic index and glycemic load values: 2002. Am. J. Clin. Nutr. 76:5-56.

Clearly implicates added sugar... Yang, Q., Z. Zhang, E.W. Gregg, D. Flanders, R. Merritt, F.B. Hu. 2014. Added sugar intake and cardiovascular disease mortality among US adults. JAMA Inter. Med. 174(4):516-524. Doi 10.1001/jamainternmed.2013.13563

The toxic truth about sugar... Lustig, RH, LA Schmidt, CD Brindis. 2012. Public Health: The toxic traits of sugar. Nature, 882:27-29. (02 Feb 2014). doi: 10.1038/482027a.

French trial to evaluate 20 different pet foods... Nguyen P., H. Dumon, V. Biorge, E. Pouteau. 1998. Glycemic and insulinemic response after ingestion of commercial foods in healthy dogs: Influence of food composition. J. Nutr. 128:2654S-2658S.

Proven in numerous diverse species... Levenson, CW, and NJ Rich. 2007. Eat less, live longer? New insights into the role of caloric restriction in the brain. Nutr. Rev. 65:412-415.

Caloric restriction in general... Kealy, R.D., DF Dennis, JM Ballum, SL Mantz, DN Biery, EH Greeley, G Lust, M Segre, GK Smith, HD Stowe. 2002. Effect of diet restriction on life span and age-related changes in dogs. J. Am. Vet. Med. Assoc. 220:1315-1320.

5

ANATOMY AND DIGESTIVE PHYSIOLOGY
(IMMUNITY AND BACTERIA, FRIENDLY AND NOT)

M y twin brother pioneered the science of drug delivery across the lung wall, culminating after years with FDA and EU approval for aerosol insulin. Every lecture he gave during the 15 years of the journey began with a particular graphic visual. It was a picture of a tennis court, which he used to illustrate the surface area of our lungs, the one drug delivery door nature left open as he put it. Our story could begin with the very same visual image, a tennis court. This is not only the surface area of our lungs, it so happens it is also the surface area of our gastrointestinal tract, and an even more open door. Any discussion about digestive physiology must rest on the vast cellular surface area involved.

A frequent failing of a writer is to aspire to tell all they know of a subject, when really what is needed is for them to say as little as possible and still convey the concept. It is recognized that physiology is not everybody's most enthralling interest, so I'll be as brief as possible.

There are several general observations about a gastrointestinal tract that need to be reviewed. A large portion of all immune capability is found in the gut. This is logical if pondered a moment, as we take in untold millions of bacteria when we eat things. Admittedly, our modern diet is quite clean compared to the days of our ancestors, but the defensive muscle echoes on yet today. I certainly am not advocating disregard for common sense when it comes to microbiology, but consider all the monogastrics of the world (single stomach animals, like you) that eat seemingly abominable meals with no ill effect. The leopard hauls its kill into a tree and leisurely gnaws on it for two days in the African sun; the stray dog makes a feast out of three day old road kill; the grizzly bear buries a sheep carcass for later retrieval because it adds to its appeal in the bear's opinion. We won't even mention vultures. This type of eating behavior, which brings in massive bacterial loads, is not greatly different from what primordial man did every day. To allow such indiscriminate eating habits, immunity in the gut had to become pronounced, and it still is today.

Why then, you ask, did you get such a persistent case of dysentery when on vacation in Mexico? The main reason is because you encountered a bacterial challenge you had not been exposed to before. The natives don't get the same affliction nearly as often. In my own experience of working in North Africa on repeated assignments, I eventually succumbed to an intestinal ailment that persisted for nine months and defied all solutions available to me in the States. Spend enough time as a visitor in an emerging economy and you'll eventually get hit. Just ask anyone who's done it.

Another reason is that often local food handling personnel in emerging economies are naïve about the rules (wash the hands, keep mayonnaise refrigerated, etc.) and also, if you think about it, you probably had a big feast, which gave the new bacteria an immense amount of substrate to grow on. Lastly, these types of problems are more likely in warmer climes, where bacteria proliferate and mutate all year and never encounter winter temperatures to curb their march.

There are outbreaks of food poisoning in modern societies. These can be very traumatic and sometimes lethal. The authorities invariably contain them quickly and identify the source of the offense. Frequently, virulent cases of food poisoning are actually the result of bacterial toxins, or waste products of the bacteria, rather than the bacteria themselves. These toxins, such as from botulism, are nearly indestructible, and remain active long after the bacteria are dead and gone. This leads to a situation where a food may appear free of bacterial contamination when scrutinized by sight or smell, but it actually is toxic. In this way, food may have been mishandled, yet appear quite wholesome upon arriving at the final kitchen. An example of this would be frozen food that thawed at some point in the supply chain, then was refrozen. Food handler education, including truck drivers, is the foundation of a safe food system.

There are over 300 million Americans eating three meals a day, which, if you count snacks, is a billion meals a day, or 365 billion a year. Yet major cases of food poisoning are not often in the news. The Centers for Disease Control and Prevention in 2007 there are 5,000 deaths a year in the U.S. from food poisoning. Many of these deaths are in the very young or very old or those with compromised immune capability. Based on this frequency of incidence, in America this means that one's odds of death by food poisoning from any one given meal are one in 73 million. Undoubtedly, there are numerous unreported diners who endure a night of grave distress due to improper food handling, but within a day are back to their normal routine. However, I think you see the point. There are a lot of meals eaten in the U.S. without any digestive calamity. It is an incredibly safe food supply. But also, part of the reason is that mammals have a tough and resilient GI tract. By design, it contains a very hardy immune defense that was perfected over billions of years of evolution.

The GI tract is itself an organization of specific tissues, and like other tissues such as muscle or bone or skin, under regular challenge undergoes hypertrophy, or enlarges. The hands can grow callused; the muscles enlarge or bones thicken under constant strain. The sumo wrestler or the pro football lineman is not a man of normal GI tract and enlarged body mass. Their GI tract is also enlarged. So is the GI tract of anyone who eats a lot, whether they are fat or not. We know that the GI tract of a dairy cow that gives large amounts of milk can be increased by 30 percent or more from its normal size.

I mention this because it is an aspect of weight loss and dieting that few consider. A successful diet not only includes the shedding of excess body fat, it also requires the shrinking of the GI tract. As anyone knows who starts a diet, and who among us has not, the GI tract protests loudly about this process. For the obese animals in our care that we choose to put on a diet, we usually do a better job of overcoming their hunger pangs than we do for ourselves. Begging by the fat dog on a diet is the same thing as the weak will power that subverts so many of us trying to diet. Just as building powerful biceps takes a lot of work in the gym, shrinking a GI tract does not happen without commitment.

We've discussed GI tracts and that they all contain a perpetual population of friendly bacteria, usually as helpful partners in the digestion process. These friendly bacteria do not seem to cause any alarm at the cellular level, and the prodigious immune defense leaves them in peace. In herbivores, the role of bacteria (and some mold and fungi) is widely recognized for its essential function in digestion. The bacteria in these animals get a warm place to live, sheltered from all storms, and are handed a meal every day. In return, they partially digest this meal, sending their leavings on to the host, as well as the metabolic byproducts of their own metabolism. All mammalian GI tracts harbor bacteria. From there, animal digestive systems divide into those with friendly and helpful bacteria predominating in the far end, like ours or dogs, and all others that have friendly and essential bacteria predominating in the front end, such as herbivores.

As an indication of the effectiveness of this strategy, consider the cockroach, one of oldest known creatures in the world, basically unchanged for over 300 million years. The primordial Lucy and her kin, the proverbial missing link of our own decent, are not even four million years old. Cockroaches have a symbiotic relationship with the bacteria in their gut. The mother cockroach inoculates her egg case so that the baby cockroaches are born with immediate use of these bacteria. If this egg case is sterilized in such a way as to kill the bacteria, the baby cockroaches still hatch, but soon die of starvation.

There is recent evidence that intestinal bacteria may be involved in our wellbeing in ways we haven't yet suspected. An article in *Nature* in 2006 reported a gut microbe fraction in skinny mice not found in obese siblings, which when introduced to fat siblings, led to weight loss. This hints at the possibility that skinny people have gut microbes that help keep them skinny, and fat people have gut microbes that help keep them fat. Indeed, there would appear to be a growing appreciation for the role of gut microbes in our daily wellbeing. It is now recognized that there are more than 10 times more bacterial cells in our GI tract than there are in our entire body, and further, the combined genetic material of our gut bacteria is over 100 times that of our own body. Of all these bacteria, 70 percent are completely unknown with regard to their physical or nutritional requirements. It seems there is a core of common bacteria found in most everybody, but there are also particular individual species, such that every person's gut microflora is unique to them, just like a fingerprint.

Classifying the different digestive systems of animals tends to parallel the relationship an animal has with bacteria. Here is a recap of the digestive classification from Chapter 2. In broad terms, the world is divided into monogastrics and herbivores. Monogastrics, as the word implies, have one stomach. People and dogs and cats are monogastrics. Herbivores typically have the adaptation of a large holding area at some point in the first half of the tract that serves as a fermentation tank where bacteria break down the plant fibers. Herbivores as a group are very diverse and include cattle, sheep, goats, deer, horses and rabbits to mention a few of the more obvious. This group also includes elephants, certain primates (so called leaf eaters) kangaroos, wildebeest and gazelles, to mention some that might not occur to you. The main reason the classification is so large is because the world's land mass is covered with plants that perpetually capture the sun's energy and are an unfailing meal if you can survive on them. Drought of course can be a problem, but there are adaptations for this, such as migration. Because plants are so reliable, evolution favored the ascendance of animals that could survive using plants as their food. Because plants are so ubiquitous and abundant, there are lots of animals that eat them. Because plants are not particularly dense in concentrations of protein or energy, herbivores have spacious GI tract adaptations to allow the consumption of large amounts of plants. An 1,100 pound herbivore on the Serengeti Plains can devour up to 150 pounds of forage in a day. In Australia, a truly fascinating laboratory of Darwinian evolution, there were no traditional herbivores, so this void was filled by the kangaroo and its relatives. *(See the fiber discussion in Chapter 2 about rabbits in Australia.)*

The teeming herbivores of the world are the private smorgasbord of the carnivore, which intermittently harvests small quantities of herbivores that are perpetually harvesting large amounts of plants. At the cellular level, the meat eaters and plant eaters do not have greatly different nutritional needs. The way the world has become organized, the carnivore in essence lets the plant eater do its grazing. When a pride of lions has killed a wildebeest and had their repast, there is nothing left. This doesn't mean all the meat is eaten and the bones and innards are left for the hyenas and vultures, even though these ambulance chasers of the plains are infamous thieves at any kill. The lions eat everything, given the chance, and in so doing, get all the benefit of what the herbivore has eaten. This allows the carnivore to obtain essential nutrients not found in pure meat tissue, and would include such nutrients as the vitamin E that is plentiful in plants, and therefore in the gut contents of herbivores. Meat tissue is woefully low in calcium, so eating bones provides for this need. The gut contents also provide a rich source of B vitamins, produced by the bacteria of the herbivore GI tract. Here we see at least part of the attraction your dog has for horse feces, a behavior that so appalls many people but is not only harmless, but even beneficial. More on vitamins is discussed in Chapter 10.

ANATOMY OF A SINGLE STOMACH ANIMAL

Figure 12 represents the anatomy of a monogastric such as man, and Figure 13 shows a dog's digestive anatomy. Food is taken into the mouth, where it is chewed into smaller pieces and mixed with saliva, which adds enzymes and aids swallowing. The food is passed to the stomach, which has an acidic pH of two to three due to the secretion of hydrochloric acid, lethal to many bacteria. The stomach mixes the food and passes it into the small intestines, where most of the breakdown and absorption of nutrition takes place. Throughout the GI tract mucus protects the intestine from abrasion by food particles and also from self digestion due to all the powerful enzyme secretions, designed precisely to attack tissue. The entire process of digestion is aided by enzymes and indeed is only possible because of them.

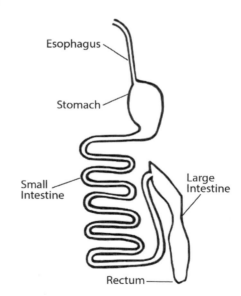

Figure 12 *Anatomy of the digestive tract of the human (monogastric).*

74

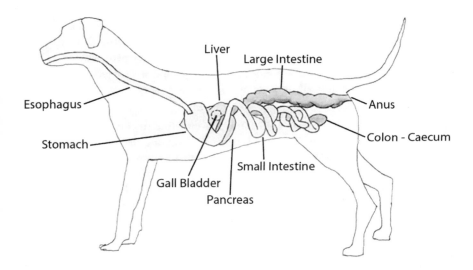

Figure 13 *Digestive anatomy of a dog*

The small intestines and accessory glands secret many enzymes that do all the heavy lifting of digestion. These enzymes are quite specific at their job, some breaking down fat, some protein, some long chains of carbohydrate units, others short chains of carbohydrate units. Some attack the end of protein amino acids chains, while some attack proteins at specific amino acids. In short, it is a marvelous and graphic demonstration of the complexity and beauty of the life process, and this small paragraph covers what is only properly covered by several volumes. Digestion is in reality numerous steps. Each of these steps recruits different enzymes and carrier proteins. This in turn involves activation of receptor sites, turning on genes, which may turn on other genes, transcription of messenger RNA and protein (enzyme) synthesis.

An illustration of one enzyme may be familiar to some. Lactase, mentioned in the section on carbohydrate, is an enzyme that assists in the digestion of the sugar found in milk, lactose. The argument is sometimes put forth that mammals are not intended, and therefore not designed to consume milk after weaning, and hence it is logical, the argument goes, that the enzyme is programmed to fade after weaning. There are some people and pets that do have lactose intolerance, but most individuals enjoy dairy products their whole life. Certain enzymes, termed inducible, are brought forth or made on the spot when the substance they digest appears in the gut. Possibly this is true for lactase, in which case a little milk all the time would be indicated. Inasmuch as milk is a quality food, this may not be a bad idea. Milk is the only thing we harvest from nature designed expressly to be food, and it is nature's most perfect food. It is recognized there is a small but ardent anti-milk contingent, separate even from vegan and vegetarians. In their zeal, these people tend to suffer from a chauvinistic and narrow minded selection of data. The subject of milk could be an entire volume in itself. Indeed, in this case, such a book was written by my father, Stuart Patton, in 2004.

The pancreas secretes a strong buffer into the intestine to counter the acidity of stomach contents entering the small intestine, increasing the pH. In the large intestine, a pH near 7.0 (neutral) is normal. The pancreas provides enzymes for the digestion of each of the three major food components, protein, fat and carbohydrate. The other major food component, fiber, is not digested by any mammalian enzymes. The bacteria of the intestine secrete fiber digesting enzymes and are responsible for what fiber is digested by monogastrics.

The battery of enzymes produced by the pancreas is kept inactive and ineffective while still in the pancreas by a compound called trypsin inhibitor. Once in the intestine, the trypsin inhibitor deactivates, allowing the enzymes to become active. It is a critical role that trypsin inhibitor plays, as these enzymes would otherwise digest the pancreas itself. In some cases of severe injury to the pancreas (car accident, horse kick), this is just what happens. It is a condition called acute pancreatitis, and it can be fatal.

Another example of the effectiveness of GI tract enzymes is evidenced by enzyme digests used in the pet food industry. In a process called autolysis, intestines and their contents are placed in a large cooker with other food industry waste, such as meat pieces and carcass trimmings. The pH is adjusted as the temperature is increased to the enzymes optimum range, essentially body temperature, and suddenly, in about one minute, the entire cooker turns to liquid. No tissue remains, having been digested by the optimized enzymes. This liquid is dried and sold at a high price for use as a pet food ingredient. Dusted on the outside of a fat coated kibble in small amounts, it commands a premium price because it is high in protein and fat, and dogs and cats love the taste. The common kitchen condiment meat tenderizer is an enzyme.

Unlike the enzymes of the pancreas, which are secreted into the GI tract contents, the majority of the enzymes of the small intestines are found in the epithelial cells that line the gut wall, and act on food substrates as they are absorbed into these cells. These epithelial cells are shed and replaced quickly to allow for rapid repair of any intestine damage, making the GI tract a high maintenance organ.

There are not many enzymes found in the large intestine, the next and last stop on our tour. One of the main roles of the large bowel is water regulation. Amphibians spend more time in water, so have a relatively undeveloped large intestine, as water retention is less critical for them. However, as evolution progressed, and amphibians crawled out onto land and became reptiles, the large intestine increased in size to accommodate the new need for the conservation of water. Normally, the material entering the large intestine is quite fluid, and water is absorbed back into the body by the large intestine, providing a means of conserving this most essential of all nutrients, and making drier feces. The large intestine is also adept at reabsorbing sodium, to the point where feces are essentially devoid of sodium, even on a high salt diet. The large bowel can also secrete significant amounts of water into the bowel, as it does in cases of bacterial infection or food poisoning. The resulting diarrhea is distressing, but hastens a cure, with the ensuing flushing of irritants and insults. The many bacteria of the large intestine are also a significant source of vitamin K and B vitamins, which can be absorbed by their host. Normal feces of monogastrics are about 30 percent bacteria on a dry weight basis.

ANATOMY OF PLANT EATERS

Figure 14 shows the basic anatomical arrangement of the GI tract of the ruminant. This is distinct from the horse, which is covered in the last section of this chapter, and later in a chapter of its own. Ruminants occupy a specific niche in the world, because by eating plants they are living off a food source that monogastrics can't digest. Of course people eat corn and vegetables, and pigs can eat alfalfa, but only herbivores can eat grass alone and thrive. This is important for several reasons. By

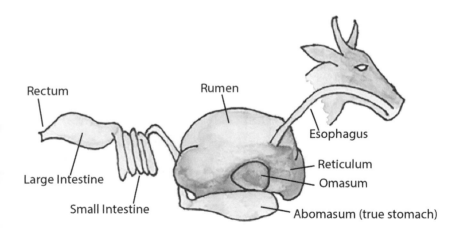

Figure 14 *Diagram of the anatomy of an herbivore such as a cow.*

subsisting on plants, the ruminant has eliminated all monogastrics as competitors, but even more critically, the ruminant does not need to compete with man for any food. This is not true for the pig and chicken, both of which are monogastrics and are no more able to digest wheat straw than is man. As population continues to grow, and more critically, as people's tastes and wherewithal permit the inclusion of more animal protein, the pressure on fertile land to grow chicken and pig foods will only increase. It will become less and less feasible to grow ruminant forage on rich soil that can also grow human foods or foods that chickens (a source of both meat and eggs) and pigs need. The ruminant will find itself relegated to the steppes and plains of the world, where climate and altitude are too severe to nurture truck crops or chicken feed, but adequate enough to grow forage for herbivores.

Presently, especially in North America, vast acreage is allotted to growing forage and grains for ruminants. These crops include alfalfa, corn, wheat, oats, barley and corn for silage, and they are grown on soils that can also be used for growing tomatoes, broccoli, carrots or garlic, all food items that in the future will pay far more return per unit of land than animal foods. If all cows were relegated to the more arid and less fertile highlands of the mountainous regions, individual animal efficiency and production will certainly decline, but the return per unit of production to the animal's owner would increase proportionally, in keeping with the laws of supply and demand, and the inelasticity of the demand for meat and milk[1]. The ruminant's innate strength, an ability to subsist on low nutrient content graze and browse, will be the reason it is banished from the rich lowlands, and the reason it survives when banished.

As a pet owner, you are probably asking yourself, of what import is all this to me? Perhaps you do not farm, or consume much meat, dairy or egg. The importance of the meat industry to the average pet owner is economic. Forty percent of the weight of a slaughtered pig or cow does not become food for people. It is byproduct, the greatest part of which goes into pet food. In this regard, the pet food industry keeps the price of meat, milk and eggs lower for the consumer. The reason is, pet foods provide a place to sell byproducts that otherwise would be a disposal expense that had to be adsorbed by the human food portion of the enterprise.

The ruminant as we all know eats grass, or if a browser, more shrubs and small bushes. This fodder after some cursory chewing is swallowed and passed to the first stomach, the rumen. The rumen is a large fermentation vat full of billions of

---

[1]*Inelasticity is an economic term that means the demand for a product is not greatly changed by a change in price. The housewife tends to buy two gallons of milk a week for her growing children. She doesn't buy more if the price goes down, and she doesn't buy less if the price goes up. Evidently gasoline is another example of inelastic demand, as a doubling of price in recent years did little to change consumption rates.*

bacteria. In the mature beef cow, it can hold 40 gallons. These bacteria thrive on the forage sent their way, and in the process of digesting it, produce metabolites used by the ruminant. Examples of these metabolites are volatile fatty acids, such as acetate (vinegar), propionate and butyrate, which cross the rumen wall and are carried in the blood to the liver, where they are converted into nutrients used by the host. There is a small but measurable amount of methane produced by herbivores, and some ecologists point to this as a burden on the environment, but in reality, the amount of methane from cows is inconsequential compared to that emitted from swamps.

The ruminant, in addition to chewing its food, also does a great deal of rechewing. Feed when first eaten and swallowed is often only partly chewed. This allows more feed to be eaten in a given period of time, which is an advantage for a prey species, but requires further processing. This the ruminant does later while lying quietly in the shadows. The technique is called rumination, and involves burping up a bolus of forage and chewing it, completely this time, then swallowing it again. The larger feed particles, the ones needing additional chewing, float on the top of the forage matt in the rumen, and are the particles eructated (what it is called when a ruminant brings a feed bolus up from its rumen to the mouth). At any one time in a group of resting ruminants, about one third can be seen chewing their cud, as it is called, or ruminating.

The typical ruminant is said to have four stomachs. After the rumen, a part of which is named the reticulum, and considered the second stomach, feed passes to the omasum and then the abomasum, the true stomach. The basic function of the rumen is to act as an admissions clerk, passing on for further digestion or holding back any feeds needing more breakdown. Mostly this is done on the basis of physical size of particles, the smaller ones falling to the floor of the rumen and passing out the opening to the omasum. The larger particles tend to float on the top of the rumen contents and are sent back up to the teeth for further grinding. In most grazing herbivores, forage is in the rumen 24 to 48 hours. Stomach retention time in dogs is reported to be a couple of hours.

Feed exits the omasum and enters the abomasum, the organ analogous to the stomach of other animals. In fact, while still nursing, the ruminant is a true and complete monogastric, and the abomasum is the stomach where milk is curdled by acid and enzymes, just as in all mammals. At about six weeks of age, the young ruminant starts to nibble on grass and the rumen soon springs into existence spontaneously, provided the right bacteria have been consumed. Should a ruminant be kept on milk, nursing from a bottle, it would reach adult size but never develop its rumen. If as an adult, a ruminant is offered milk from a bottle, the act of suckling from a bottle causes a reflex closing of the passage to the rumen, shunting the suckled liquid directly into the abomasum. The reflexive ability to selectively shunt to the abomasums seems to be retained in some herbivores as adults. Once past the rumen, digestive physiology is similar between the ruminant and the monogastric, with the small intestine and its accessory glands, and the large intestine, performing much the same role.

Figure 15 is a schematic of the horse's digestive tract. The equine is in a class of herbivore called hindgut fermenter, with emphasis on high feed intake to compensate for low nutrient density of the feed. The elephant and rhino are in this group. In the horse there is no paunch or rumen before the small intestine. Instead, the major fiber digesting occurs after the small intestine, in the cecum and large intestine, or colon, where fiber digesting bacteria are abundant. Combining superior agility and therefore food gathering ability with an efficient fiber digestion capacity, the horse is a most adept survivor. *The horse is covered in detail in Chapter 8.*

Figure 15 *Anatomy of the digestive tract of the horse. Note the close proximity of the end of the small intestine, the beginning of the large intestine and the cecum.*

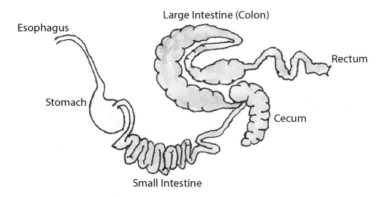

REFERENCES

The surface area of our gastrointestinal... Helander, HF, and Fändriks L. 2014. Surface area of the digestive tract-revisited. *Scand. J. Gastroenterol.* 49:681-689.

5,000 food poisonings a year... Centers for Disease Control. 2007. Atlanta, GA. www.cdc. gov/ncidod/eid/vol5no5/mead.htm

gut microbe fractions in skinny mice... Turnbaugh PJ, Ley RE, Mahowald MA, Magrini V, Mardis ER, Gordon JI. 2006. An obesity-associated gut microbe with increased capacity for energy harvest. *Nature* (Dec 21/28). 444:1027-1031. *(see also page 1022, Human gut microbes associate with obesity, by the same authors.)*

DNA in our gut over 100 times that in our body... Lenoir-Wijnkoop I, Sanders ME, Cabana MD, et al. 2007. Probiotic and Prebiotic Influence Beyond the Intestinal Tract. *Nutr. Rev.* 65: 469-489.

book written by my father... Patton, S. 2004. Milk. Its Remarkable Contribution to Human Health and Well-being. Transaction Publishers. New Brunswick (U.S.A.) and London (U.K).

6

NUTRITION AND ANIMAL BEHAVIOR

Animal behavior can be so subtle yet have dramatic effect. I was standing in front of the large cat exhibit at the Woodland Park Zoo in Seattle with the late Dr. Jim Foster when he directed me to look at a cat cowering in the corner, but I looked at the wrong animal. He redirected my gaze to a big cat hiding behind some logs, and this cat was indeed in full fear mode, ears pinned, eyes glowering at the veterinarian. Jim said there could be 200 people in front of this exhibit and that cat would spy him and hide in fear. There was nothing wrong with that cat, he told me, and he had never touched it. He then pointed out an older female he often anesthetized for medical treatment. During these treatments, whenever this cat saw Dr. Foster coming, she became all agitated and proceeded to thrash the other cat. The other cat never knew why, but whenever Dr. Foster came near, he got mauled by the intended patient. All cured, the older female was long over any concern about the veterinarian's proximity, but the other cat seemed to be scared for life – the subtle, dramatic effect of behavior and conditioning.

If you consider that nutrition problems are very rare in the wild, yet a frequent problem for animals in captivity, you must ask yourself what is the logical source of these problems. This holds true across numerous species. Exotic birds can be afflicted with iron storage disease of unknown cause, horses with leg weakness, cattle with foot rot, cats with urolithiasis, dogs with hip dysplasia, tropical fish with infectious disease. All seem to suffer obesity and poor reproduction. The common denominator is domestication, or to be more correct, altered natural behavior due to people.

Even for people, there is evidence that altered natural behavior was associated with the loss of health. As we've seen, reports in the archeological records show that until the agricultural revolution 10,000 years ago, few suffered malnutrition. There was lack of total nutrition on occasion, but rarely problems due to imbalanced nutrient intake. After the advent of crop domestication, skeletal remains often show signs of malnutrition. The unbalanced nature of the modernized diet is considered a given, while the behavior attending the primordial diet is ignored, and wrongly so.

Aside from nutrient composition, foraging does three critical things: It improves fitness, consumes calories and offers up sustenance in small frequent amounts. Eating the daily caloric allotment at once can cause a detrimental endocrine response that the same calories eaten slowly over the day would not. Behavior can make a difference.

The vast majority of nutrition problems encountered in animals are caused by people, either from loving their animals to death or ignorance, or both. Admittedly, people invariably want more than anything to feed the correct diet, but lack information. Every zoo nutritionist has the ambition of delivering correct nutrition, and uses as a guide what the species eats in the wild. This can be impossible to deliver.

As an example, consider elephants in a city zoo. If turned loose on the city parks, even a small band of elephants in one summer would obliterate every tree and shrub in sight, and of course have no fresh browse in winter. So compromise is applied. Grass hay fed to the elephants will keep them alive, but it is a sad substitute for daily fresh browse. Due to exquisite adaptability, found in all species, the elephants survive, but do they thrive? If the elephants are to live 50 years in captivity, as in the wild, a diet of grass hay is counter productive. Reports cited by Crawford indicate elephants relegated to the grass of the plains in Africa suffered from hardening of the arteries, an affliction nonexistent in elephants of the forest.

There is a tendency to think of behavior as a conscious decision involving such concepts as delayed gratification, stimulus-reward or prioritizing desires. The word behavior easily attaches in our minds with words like aggressive, friendly or submissive, each viewed as a conscious choice. But the word behavior is just as easily invoked for mating. A male dog near a female in heat has very little choice in the behavior the bitch elicits from him. There is no clear distinction between behavior and physiology. A male dog that is restrained by mere voice commands from sniffing obsessively after a bitch in estrus is referred to interchangeably as well trained or well behaved. Much of what is referred to as behavior is training to suppress what is driven by normal physiology, often referred to as innate behavior. On more than one occasion I watched a mountain lion devour an entire rib cage, easily crushing the flat bones, only to retire elsewhere and regurgitated the entire meal, which was then re-consumed at leisure. Related to this is the habit many have observed, in both dogs and cats, of eating grass. I have never encountered a credible explanation for this, but I do accept it as normal behavior, sometimes associated with inducing regurgitation.

How do dogs and cats behave when free to be themselves? Canines in the wild do not wait for 10 hours in their den for their masters to come home and feed them their only meal of the day. Wild dogs don't run and exercise for 20 minutes a day and urinate and defecate once a day during this 20 minutes. Fox hounds routinely run 40 kilometers (25 miles) in three hours. Sled dogs burn 11,000 calories a day. I don't suggest your dog needs this amount of exercise, but I do ask you to put in perspective that your dog's 20 minutes of exuberant dashing about while you trudge around the park lost in your own thoughts does not begin to address a dog's potential for exercise.

Absent human intervention, dogs hunt in packs, and cats hunt alone (lions and sometimes cheetahs being exceptions). Cats eat 10 to 20 meals a day, regardless of day or night, while dogs eat four to eight times, mostly during daylight. Cats drink less than dogs, although both will reduce drinking significantly if eating wet food (75 percent moisture). One report shows cats can maintain normal hydration on sea water. This may be somehow involved with the metabolism of the cat that does not show salt craving, even if sodium deficient. This would make the cat an exception to most all species. The dog and especially the cat do not have a clear circadian rhythm. They don't exclusively sleep at night and move about in daylight, or the reverse, like a bat. Cats can be active at night, hunting rodents, and equally predacious hunting birds the next day. One wonders if coyotes ever sleep, heard howling all night and seen throughout the next day slinking everywhere.

It would appear that taste preference in both dogs and cats is not a matter of learning what to eat, but just the opposite – of learning what not to eat, or taste aversion (just as for horses, discussed in Chapter 8). Such an approach would seem to be a good fit with the broader strategy of species survival, it being more successful to consider anything animal or vegetable as fair game and to learn the few exceptions.

Both dogs and cats fed only one diet as youngsters grow up to be inflexible about change, and hard to entice to eat new foods. It is advisable to provide different brands and types of foods (fresh, canned and dry) to puppies and kittens, when they are more opportunistic in their approach to food. As adults, they are much more accepting of different foods if fed a variety as weanlings. Based on dentition, dogs are more in the class of carnivores, but metabolically, they share certain traits with omnivores and herbivores and are different from the cat. The dog, but not the cat, can convert β-carotene into vitamin A, tryptophan into niacin, cysteine into taurine and linoleate into arachidonate (Chapter 9 on the cat has more).

Dogs, similar to the rat, show a taste preference for protein, and are able to discriminate between a low and high protein food. Cats lack this ability, which at first seems incongruous. From an evolutionary point of view, however, this is logical for a carnivore that never ate anything that wasn't high in protein. A carnivore may suffer from a lack of all nutrients in hard times, but never for a lack of protein compared to other nutrients. Both dogs and cats show a taste preference for fat, certain peptides in the form of enzyme hydrolysates dusted on the outside of foods and for certain free amino acids. Dogs like umami, a flavor related to monosodium glutamate (MSG).

Behavior is a major component of nutrition. Allow one illustration. Several years ago I was consulting for a zoo with a fine collection of primates housed in a once modern but now outdated facility. It was constructed in an era when disease spread between people and animals was a leading concern, so the animal enclosures were all ceramic tile and glass barriers, or otherwise material that could be washed, hosed and sterilized. The result was just that, an animal enclosure that was sterile. The entire collection had bad hair coats, from the little capuchins and tamarins to chimps. I promptly suggested the feed additives that always cured such problems, specifically zinc and copper in both chelate and inorganic form, sulfur containing amino acids, gelatin, dried egg and the real winner, fish oil (for omega-3 fatty acids). Nothing happened. Hair coats were unaffected, and remained dry, brittle and thin. Skin was scaly and the species with long hair covered tails looked like rats in some cases. I was puzzled. My hair coat cure had always worked before.

Some time prior to this the keepers had taken to putting hay all over the concrete floors of the exhibits in an attempt to soften the jail cell nature of the space. One day a keeper forgot to include the peanuts in the daily ration and belatedly tossed them onto the hay of each exhibit. The primates immediately found and ate every peanut. But then the keepers noticed something. Even after all the peanuts were found and eaten, the monkeys kept looking for them, as if driven by some long pent up urge to behave like monkeys. The keepers of course were delighted with this turn of events, as all zoo professionals are quite concerned with achieving normal behavior in their charges. Every day they tossed several handfuls of peanuts into the hay on the floor of every exhibit, and at any hour one could see primates searching in the hay for peanuts. Within a week, hair coats started to improve and in two months were restored to their full luster. The missing essential nutrient had been behavior.

Dogs are omnivores. Or said another way, they easily can default to omnivore behavior. If you doubt this, come with me on a walk in any direction from my house. I will show you coyote feces that contain the expected mouse remains, but also juniper berries, grass, pine nuts, apple cores and candy wrappers. We can intuit that the coyote did not find these things to eat all in one place at 6:30 in the evening. He moved, off and on all night, and during the day as well, if needed. This is normal, primordial behavior for the canine. To the extent that you can provide smaller meals more often, it is better.

Everyone trains animals using treats. The behavior we want is rewarded, or as psychologist would say, reinforced. All have heard of Pavlov's dog, and the connection between stimulus and response. Human rights advocates would decry that it is our inadequacy that drives us to dominate animals with behavior modification. But within their own natural world, absent any human intervention, behavior is shaped emphatically. The mother wolf punishes bad behavior (negative reinforcement) and encourages good behavior (positive reinforcement). Learning what behavior improves life is the very essence of survival. Discriminating between action that makes life better and action that makes life worse is instinctual in all creatures. Even an amoeba can be trained.

In the familiar world of animal training, a stimulus is only as useful as the animal's interest in it. This is why food treats are common as training aids, as most animals are interested in food. We've all seen the animal trainers at Sea World with the belt box of handy, frequently applied treats. Falconers use the same ready offering of meat tidbits to train raptors. However, there can be a wide range of effectiveness in this reward method.

I once had a Bloodhound, who even if he was starving and you had a raw steak, would not come when called. On the other hand, we had an Australian Shepherd that would not go through a door without first looking at you for permission. Willingness to please the master is a hard wired trait for the most part, an innate aspect of personality, and it can be high or low, even among litter mates. Consequently, the behavior of patience on the part of the trainer needs to be more, or less, in accordance.

There is another important interface between animal and trainer behavior that is not quite as obvious. Occasional rewards are actually more effective than constant rewards. The professionals say this as "intermittent reinforcement takes longer for extinction." When first shaping your dog's behavior to come when called, morsels are given with every successful obedience. But you know this can't go on the dog's entire life. Soon, you reduce the reward to lavish praise, but no treat, and in due time, the dog's reward is little more than a pat on the head or cursory rub of the ears. If the dog sometimes gets a morsel when he comes, and sometimes not, he is willing to look at the process as a lottery, knowing it sometimes doesn't pay but eventually will if he hangs in there. If an assured reward suddenly stops, the dog quickly backslides in the behavior shaping, seeing no rationale in investing in an unrewarding effort.

Behavior can be far more subtle than we realize. Your pet can tell unfailingly from the cadence and force of your footfall if you are going to the bathroom, to work for the day or to feed them. To them it is no different than a public address announcement, but completely lost on us. Seabiscuit became a very successful racehorse, but not until his new owners realized that he did exactly what he had been trained to do, push other favorites in training races but come in second himself. I nearly exhausted myself in a failed effort to train a horse to come to my whistle, only to learn that the horse in the next stall had learned it perfectly. Behavior lessons taught to me by polar bears and primates were endlessly insightful, once I got over the embarrassment.

I consider this the single most important rule of animal behavior: the keeper trains the monkey, not the monkey the keeper. It can be amazing how quickly our animals train us, and we don't even know it. I once formulated a diet for primates, presumably balanced if eaten entirely, that was a delightful array of fruits, vegetables and a commercial biscuit. The monkeys of course preferred the fruits and vegetables, and left the less palatable biscuit uneaten. As a matter of fact, they took to throwing the biscuits at the keepers, along with other missiles close at hand such as fecal clumps. The keepers were not about to be wasteful of zoo budget, let alone tolerate such monkey business, and stopped offering the biscuit. It took two days for the monkeys to train the keepers to substitute more fruit for biscuits.

Our pets do the same thing. If they don't eat the food we offer, our first inclination is to try a different food in hopes that they like it better. I promise you if you remove refused food and offer it again in a few hours, it will get closer consideration. In due time, it will be eaten. Besides, if our concept of palatability for dogs was so learned, why do nearly all dogs relish horse feces, the fresher the better? Few of us have the resolve to outlast our pets, especially once they catch on that you will bring something different if they refuse what you offer.

A cliché of community solidarity is the scenario of the firemen called to retrieve a kitten from the upper reaches of a tree. I'll never forget the time I happened upon such a rescue and was visiting with one of the fireman, a kindly old veteran. He smiled as he observed that in his long career he had never seen a cat skeleton in a tree. Kittens find a way down out of the tree, and no animal will voluntarily starve itself to death in the presence of anything resembling food.

We once converted an entire collection of large cats to a dry food, with one exception. The lions, tigers and leopards all took to consuming the dry biscuit, albeit reluctantly, and maintained weight. But not the bobcats. They never touched the first morsel, and lost weight until it seemed they were nothing but ears and feet. One day a zoo keeper informed me he had seen the bobcats catching song birds in their enclosure. We put all the cats back on a balanced fresh meat diet. We'd proved our point, and so had the bobcats.

Our neighbors had a Shih Tzu that was a cranky old bitch, often snapping at visitors. But they loved her. She had trained them to cook chicken and liver for her every day, and they were convinced she would not eat anything else. Additionally, she had a debilitating illness, and they were of the conviction that twice a day medication was essential for her life. One day, during a house sitter's watch, this dog escaped and disappeared. Days of frantic searching gave way to the sad resignation she had been killed by coyotes, a very real prospect, and a long period of grieving began. Weeks later the dog turned up, in perfect health. In our community of 100 homes 30 miles from anywhere, she had never been seen. It is suspected she had lived on her own in the high desert, but regardless, she certainly did not have twice daily sautéed chicken or any medication. She was promptly returned to her precise regimen of cooked meat and meds, and died in a week.

The secret to a long and productive life, for ourselves as well as our pets, is to expand the behavior that adds vitality and avoid behavior that compromises vigor. This requires careful reasoning and long thoughtful observation, as the world is full of sinister traps, like sugar, that taste so good, but will lead inexorably to ill health if eaten to excess. Avoid hasty conclusions and watch constantly for the hidden conditioning. Where have your beloved pets leveraged your affection for them into you killing them with kindness?

REFERENCES

plains elephants suffer hardening of arteries... Crawford, M., and D Marsh. 1989. *The Driving Force. Food, evolution and the future. Harper and Row. New York. pg 143.*

cats can maintain normal hydration... Wolf, AV. 1959. *Potability of sea water with special reference to the cat. Am. J. Physiol. 196: 663-641.*

cat does not show salt craving... Yu, S., QR Rogers, JG Morris. 1997. *Absence of a salt (NaCl) preference or appetite in sodium-replete or depleted kittens. Appetite 2: 1-10.*

Dog and cat do not have circadian rhythm... Hawkings, FM, C Lobban, K. Gamage, MJ Worms. 1971. *Circadian rhythms (activity, temperature, urine and microfilariae) in dog, cat, hen, duck, Thamnomys and Gerbillus. J. Interdiscpl. Cycle Res. 2:455-473...and* Randall, W., RF Johnson, S Randall, TJ Cunningham. 1985. *Circadian rhythms in food intake and activity in domestic cats. Behav. Neursci. 99: 1162-1175.*

hard to entice to eat new foods... Kuo, ZY. 1967. *The Dynamics of Behavior Development: An Epigenetic View. Random House. New York.*

cats lack protein discrimination... Cook, NE, QR Rogers, JG Morris. 1996. *Acid-base balance affects dietary choice in cats. Appetite 26: 175-192.*

both dogs and cats show a taste preference... Hargrove, DM, JG Morris, QR Rogers. 1994. *Kittens choose a high lysine diet even when isoleucine and valine are the limiting amino acids. J. Nutr. 124: 689-693.*

7

THE FEEDING OF
MICROBIALS AND BACTERIA

As we have perfected the tilling of the soil, eliminating all plants but one in a vast acreage, it would appear we have simultaneously decimated microbial diversity. A corn field has one type of plant and 200 species of microbes in the soil. Meanwhile, the native prairie right beside it has 100 plants and up to 8000 species in the soil. What might be the comparison of the gut micro flora of a family pet on canned food and a wolf or even feral dog? The coyote spends its entire life on undisturbed natural soil, consuming bacteria by the millions. The family pet lives his entire life in a sanitized house eating sterile food (if canned).

Microbes are of great importance to human food programs. Yogurt is full of microbes. Microbes give us beer, wine and spirits. Besides growing little blue disks on the cheese in the back of the refrigerator, microbes enable bread and make sauerkraut. The ancient Egyptians changed the entire face of farming and animal domestication when they invented silage, the preserving and storing of wet crops, with fermentation by microbes. I mentioned earlier the incredible number of microbes in the human gut, being over 10 times the number of cells in our entire body. There should be nothing strange to us about adding microbes, or their byproducts, to animal food. Not only health food stores and drug stores but even neighborhood grocery stores offer countless opportunities to buy foods that contain live bacteria. It is not a big leap for people eating probiotics to see merit in giving such products to their pets.

Most people are comfortable with the concept of feeding microbes, or probiotics as they are called. It is commonplace, for example, to turn to yogurt to aid in recovery from a bout of diarrhea. The lactobacillus in yogurt, a cultured dairy product, is widely considered as friendly bacteria. Often a doctor will prescribe a round of oral antibiotics and suggest that yogurt, or some other probiotic product, be eaten afterwards to help repair the carnage the antibiotic created among the friendly bacteria of the gut.

Early on in my career, a young salesman came to our labs to tell me about his company's yeast extract product. He introduced me to his product with a graphic little show-and-tell. He took one of our dog foods and put some in two bowls with water. In one bowl he added a thimble size scoop of his yeast extract, and in a few minutes, the kibble turned to mush. The food in the other bowl with only water was barely changed for over 30 minutes. What he was demonstrating, principally, was the effect of enzymes.

Another illustration from my experience of the magic of enzymes was an old gelding named, oddly, Marge. Marge was the consummate school horse, taking the most timid novice and instilling confidence in them while he wisely and patiently did exactly what the instructor asked despite what the confused rider did. But Marge had become so old and debilitated that nothing done for him in the way of feed would keep weight on him. One of his main afflictions was that he had very few teeth. We added a good enzyme supplement to his feed and we extended his useful, contented life for over a year. The product contained enzymes and bacteria that helped him digest, or more correctly pre-digested, the fiber component of his ration.

For many years now, feed tags have dutifully carried long strange names of probiotics that are mixed in the formula. Most everyone has read these terms, or at least looked at them, and presumed or hoped the feed professionals knew what they were doing. Such ingredients as lactobacillus acidophilus, aspergillus oryzae, and bacillus subtilis are literally Greek to most of us, and they are only three of thousands upon thousands of microbes. While regulatory officials enforce strict guidelines for feed safety everywhere there is applicable science, the problem is the vast universe of the unknown about bacteria. Every mouthful of every feed is covered with bacteria, all part of the world we live in, and only very rarely is it a problem. It is this broad tolerance that animals have for ingested bacteria that provides cover for probiotic peddlers whose entrepreneurial zeal exceeds their scientific veracity.

Suppose we were to focus on one of the Latin names encountered on a food label, for example, *Aspergillus oryzae*, and follow this back up the marketing chain, asking each person encountered "what is this ingredient, what does it do, and what is the proof?" We can pretty well assume the salesman could not answer these three questions. The store owner would not know. The manufacturer and the company marketing director would probably refer us to the formulator, or nutritionist. The nutritionist hopefully would have a general idea of why he included this ingredient, but not likely proof the ingredient is efficacious. For solid proof of efficacy, our next stop, and best hope, would be the source of the ingredient, the wholesaler of *Aspergillus oryzae*, who may rummage in his files and produce scientific articles on feeding *A. Oryzae* to dogs, cats or horses. Not likely. Probably he would pass us on to the manufacturer or grower and harvester of the microbe. At this point, we have slipped further from our goal, as this last person is an expert on growing bugs and not inclined to worry about its final effect in each creature his many downstream customers target.

The publishers of *Feedstuffs*, a weekly periodical for agribusiness, assembled a compendium of all the known and willing manufacturers of what they classed as direct fed microbials (MicrobialCompendium.com), meaning supplements of a microbial nature that are intended to be fed to animals. There are multinational corporations that produce and market nothing but direct fed microbials. The categories listed are bacteria, enzymes, molds, oligosaccharides and yeast. The products total 588. There is some duplication in this number, as some products contain combinations of these categories, and a few existing companies are not included. But it should be evident from the size of this compendium that microbial additives are a well established market segment that did not arrive at this level of prominence by subterfuge or deceit. Many of these products make a useful and measurable contribution to animal diets. The animal owner's dilemma (surprise, surprise) is to identify the useful ones.

PROBIOTICS

The term "probiotic" is encountered frequently these days but it is not a safe assumption that it means the same thing to all who hear the word. There are several official definitions for the term probiotic, and the different regulatory bodies concerned in the United States (FDA, CDC, USDA) do not share a full consensus. So for the record, we should define what probiotic actually means in this discussion. As the name implies, it is the opposite of antibiotic in that probiotics are friendly bacteria, or more correctly, microbes. In all definitions, the common denominator of a probiotic is a microbe that is added to the feed that has a beneficial effect on the animal's wellbeing. While antibiotic has a fairly narrow meaning, probiotic is not quite as tidy a concept. Part of the disparity is that some official definitions specify "live." Yet some effective products are not live cells, but extracts thereof that serve as nutrients or promote the growth of other microbes. Probiotic can mean microbe cells that are attenuated, or dormant, but become active in the gut. Adding to this array of possibilities is the further confusion of the meaning of the word microbe itself. Yeast, mold, fungus and bacteria are all microbes, and each can be used as a source of probiotics.

Thus, unofficially, probiotic can mean many things. It can refer to dried nutrients extracted from yeast, or dead bacteria or live molds. For the purpose of this discussion, let probiotic have the following meaning: Any kind of microbe, live or dead, whole or in part, that when fed to an animal has beneficial effects. I appreciate that regulatory officials must have clear definitions that are unequivocal at the point of enforcement. We all benefit from this. But in reality an animal owner is little concerned with the technical description of an additive and quite interested in its effect. Botulism toxin made by live clostridium is frightfully lethal long after the microbe it came from is dead, a fact of no consolation to anyone whose loved one was a victim of this toxin. So how does one make sense of it all? It is not easy, as these ingredients, used in miniscule amounts, can be subtle in effect.

There are some basic measurements to look for. The regulations specify live or viable microbes, which are to be disclosed on the label, such as lactobacillus acidophilus or enterococcus faecium. Their inclusion rate is spelled out by stating the colony forming units (CFUs) that are added. One CFU is a single microbe or reproducible unit such as a spore that can be placed in a culture medium and grow into a full colony of identical, live bugs. In other words, it is supposed to indicate live microbes. In reality, it is often abused. One reason being it is an onerous task for the authorities to police. To sleuth out the label CFUs from all the other bacteria likely to be in a feed is a job for an experienced, sophisticated lab. Focusing on CFUs can add to the confusion, as there are numerous probiotics that are not live or viable, but have been sold in the marketplace for decades. These types of products are extracts of microbe fermentation and contain some or all of the different parts of the organism. Some may be only the cell contents, and others may be the cell wall, or part of the cell wall, with or without the cell contents. These are usually classed as prebiotics, discussed below.

The gastrointestinal tract, with its gut-associated lymphoid tissue such as tonsils, Peyer's patches and adenoids, is a major player in the body's immune defense. This is not surprising, as the gut is evolved and perfected to tolerate the intake of vast bacterial loads. The immune system of each and every creature has an incredible and mysterious ability called "recognition of self." It is what keeps our immune system from attacking our own cells, and its failing is the fundamental indicator of autoimmune disease of all types. But this leads to an intriguing question. How does the powerful immune defense of the gut recognize as "friendly" the millions of bacteria in the gut? And how does it differentiate friends from pathogens?

The mechanism is not well understood, but experts in the field quietly explore the benefit of probiotics on immune response. I say quietly because any health claim must be proved to the satisfaction of the FDA, a long, exacting and very expensive process. Gloria Solano-Aguilar at ARS in Beltsville, MD, has made progress. In the presence of probiotics in the gut, research by Solano-Aguilar has shown immune response in pigs is improved. *For more on probiotics, see End Notes page 167.*

The age or condition of an animal can greatly influence the effect of a probiotic. Timing of application can be crucial so this too must be established before market rollout. There are products that work in several situations, but most are quite specific. Some must be introduced at birth, and these actually are usually better fed to the mother before birth. In this way, tiny particles of feed and traces of feces contaminate the environment with the friendly bug, and the newborn consumes the bug when it nurses or when the mother licks it. Other probiotics only work in growing animals or sick and ailing animals. Some work in the small intestine, others in the colon. Some only work in mature animals or in animals living in a "dirty" environment like a shabby pet store, or in animals under stress, such as after surgery, or those struggling to survive in a puppy mill farm. Remember, "work" means show a measurable benefit.

As mentioned, there are effective products of long standing in the market place that belong in this discussion, but don't strictly fit the definition of being alive. Maybe these microbe extracts, or fermentation products as they are usually called, belong in the next segment of the discussion, prebiotics.

PREBIOTICS

A prebiotic is generally considered an ingredient that supports or helps a probiotic, or friendly bacteria, already in the gut. These are less studied substances, and include such plant or microbe compounds as inulin and oligosaccharides. Some microbe extracts fall into this category by default, merely because they are not live or viable, and are excluded from the definition of a probiotic. Others belong is this group by definition. One example would be fructo-oligosaccharides, called FOS, found in garlic, asparagus and artichokes, as well as thousands of other plants, but there are no mammalian enzymes that break down this molecule. However, when fed to animals, including people, this compound promotes the growth in the gut of special bacteria that can digest it. This bacteria, or the FOS, has been shown to provide benefits, including improving the health of the epithelial lining of the intestine. It was reported to reduce intestinal pathogens and flatulence in dogs, which many pet owners would welcome.

Research has shown that animals fed FOS have increased friendly bacteria, less pathogens, improved mineral absorption and improved fecal odor. Another prebiotic of growing interest is MOS (mannan-oligosaccharide). MOS is believed to actively participate in pathogen binding in a process referred to as competitive exclusion, a process well understood by the drug industry. It is suspected that compounds like MOS, or the bacteria they promote, offer pathogenic bacteria a binding site and escort them to their undoing, or deny pathogens a binding site, resulting in their being flushed from the body.

To include MOS in a pet food and claim competitive exclusion promptly brings up the radar of the regulatory folks, as they consider this a distinct health claim, which is not allowed. It is legal to include MOS or MOS-containing ingredients in pet food, but you may not say anything (meaning claim on the label) about pathogen binding. Ongoing research is revealing additional benefits of MOS, so it may soon be possible to include MOS in pet foods and advertise other benefits of value to pet owners, such as perhaps reduced fecal odor.

It is agreed by many that some prebiotics and probiotics fed orally are somehow helpful, but the scientific community is far from satisfied that there is enough known (meaning published referee journal research) about most products regarding location of effect in the gut, size and timing of the dose, or age and circumstance of the target animal. One can be confident that no harmful pre- or probiotic makes it to the market place, and most are helpful in at least some circumstances. Probiotics are much like prescription drugs in that once you stop feeding them, the benefits soon stop. There are a few that might colonize the gut forevermore with one dose, but this is quite rare. It is a needless step to top dress a supplement on a feed if it is possible to find the supplement already included in a commercial food.

Dry foods that list microbes in their ingredients and disclose the number of CFUs added, would in theory be better than those that do not. So too for feeds that disclose they include fermentation extract. These, correctly, would not mention CFU, but can be just as effective. Canned products that list fermentation extracts are suspect, because the temperatures of cooking are so high that most enzymes are denatured. However, if only CFU plate counts are the criteria, the track record in the market place for label compliance by probiotic containing products is not that stellar.

Buying a separate supplement to add to the diet has some advantage. It can be added and withdrawn, allowing quasi-scientific observations. A pet owner should have specific endpoints for comparison, such as stool firmness or coat condition. No visible response does not mean the product is useless. The more stressful or challenging the circumstance (post-surgery, crowded unclean kennel) the greater the likelihood a response will be evident. Pets that eat raw diets or have the run of the farm are less likely to show a response. These are the ones that indulge the habit of most all dogs to relish horse manure, eat grass and otherwise send billions of bacteria into their GI system.

REFERENCES

native prairie right beside it has 100 plants... Horner-Devine et al. 2004. Proc. R. Soc. Lond. B 271:113-122. from Torsvik, et al. 2002. Prokaryotic Diversity. Science. 296:1064-66.

incredible number of microbes in the human gut... Lenoir-Wijnkoop, I., Sanders ME, Cabana MD, et al. 2007. Probiotic and Prebiotic influence beyond the intestinal tract. Nurtr. Rev. 65:469-489.

explore the benefit of probiotics on immune response... Viera, A.T., Maura, F.S. Martins. 2013. The Role of Probiotics and Prebiotics in Gut Immunity. Front. Immunol. 4:4445. doi 10.3389/fimmu.2013.0045

reduce intestinal pathogens and flatulence... Terada A., H Hara, M Kataoka, T Mitsuoka. 1992. Effect of dietary lactosucrose on fecal flora and fecal metabolites of dogs. Microb. Ecol. Health Dis. 5:43-50... and Terada, A., H Hara, S Kato, T Kimura, I Fujimoti, K Hara, T. Maruyama, T Mitsuoka. 1993. Effect of lactosucrose (4-f-α-D-galactosylsucrose) on fecal flora and fecal putrefactive products of cats. J. Vet. Med. Sci. 55:291-295.

fed FOS have increased friendly bacteria... Wenk, C. 2006. in Recent advances in Pet Nutrition; p50-51. D.K. Laue and L.A. Tucker, eds. Nottingham University Press.

8

NUTRITION OF THE HORSE
STOIC BUT FRAGILE

The horse is a genuine marvel of hardiness. In the wilds of an environment as harsh as the Great Basin of central Nevada, it not only survives, but thrives, producing offspring at a rate that horse owners only dream about. Mustangs in the wild don't crib or chew on tree stumps, they don't tie up, founder or colic. Despite no shelter, neither bitter cold nor intense heat is a problem for any except the geriatric. Realistically, we must admit that most of the problems we encounter in our domesticated equines are the result of our intrusion on their innate behavior. A young stud in a corral with a mare and her new foal will be viciously attacked by the mare. On the open plains, he would flee to safety as the mare doesn't want him dead, just gone.

Nutritionally, wild horses of all ages eat from the same menu and mature without bone development problems or impaired growth. They don't ever see the first mouthful of alfalfa, grain or supplement. Of course, this is not to ignore that domesticated horses are at the mercy of their human captors, who are forced to replicate the natural environment as best as possible. Also, sometimes more is asked of the modern horse than its wild ancestor. But the point is, the nutritional needs of the horse are not difficult to provide. Water and grass pasture are all that are required, with the critical modifiers of spacious grass pasture and companions. In other words, in a small paddock, with no other horses, normal horse behavior is not possible, and problems can show up that are nutritional in origin if we don't provide a balanced diet. However, just as often, problems can show up that are nutritional but are not nutritional in origin. Frequently they are behavioral and simply evidence themselves as a nutrition problem. For example, cribbing is just as often from boredom as it is a mineral deficiency.

But let's assume we are fortunate and our horses run in happy bands in boundless grass pastures. In other words, we are able to minimize people's intrusion on normal behavior. No horse in this situation needs 20 percent protein, an amount to be found in some commercial grains. Even a team of mules pulling a plow for six hours a day, which is more work than any modern horse ever performs, does not need 20 percent protein. In the following paragraphs, I'll discuss the basic nutritional requirements of the horse, with a few additional comments on specific topics of popular concern.

THE FEEDING STRATEGY OF THE HORSE

As we've discussed, the world of mammals is divided into two basic food gathering strategies, herbivore and monogastric. People, dogs and cats are monogastrics, meaning they have one stomach, and are not proficient fiber digesters. Herbivores have a specialized gastrointestinal system that adapts them to obtain all their nutrition from plentiful and easily encountered plants. The trade-off they make is that they have to eat large amounts of these plants because, due to high fiber content, plants are low in nutrition density. To accomplish this compromise, nature provides the herbivore with a special advantage. Herbivores technically don't eat to feed themselves, they eat to feed the bacteria in their gut. Each cow or antelope or elk is actually sending its browse and forage to a paunch or rumen that is a big fermentation tank full of bacteria. The bacteria produce enzymes that digest the plant fiber into lower order molecules that are sent to the small intestine where they are absorbed for nourishment, the same as in the monogastric dog or person. Also, the bacteria themselves can serve as a source of nourishment to the host animal.

The horse is a herbivore, but its intestines have a further specialization that make the horse a unique subdivision of herbivores. The grass that the horse eats does not go first to a fermentation chamber like the cow, but to the stomach and small intestines, just like in monogastrics. The horse's adaptation is what is called a functional cecum. This is actually an organ analogous to the human appendix, but in the horse it can hold up to 20 gallons or more, unlike our appendix that is essentially nonfunctional. So the horse's answer to the front end paunch of the cow is a large cecum and lower bowel which uses the same symbiotic relationship with bacteria. Horses are sometimes referred to as hind gut fermenters, a category that includes the rhino, a relative of the horse.

This leaves the horse as a curious in-between sort of creature: the small intestine is the major site of absorption, as in all mammals, but in the horse, the major site of forage digestion, the cecum, is past the small intestine. According to our understanding of the order of things, the horse should not function, but quite obviously, the horse is wholly unconcerned with our confusion and functions just fine.

The chances are that when we do more fully understand how the horse's nutritional biochemistry works, we will see that it derives a portion of its energy from volatile fatty acids, much like the ruminant, but in the horse's case, from the cecum and large intestine, not the rumen. In all other herbivores, and certain monogastrics, volatile fatty acids of bacterial origin are a significant component of the host's energy scheme. Our larger challenge is to first understand the proper role of forage, in its different forms, and secondly, the contribution of grain to the horse's diet.

FORAGE

Just as for man and dog, the horse's metabolic machinery is ill prepared to deal with constant high intake of soluble carbohydrate (starch and sugar). The world in which the horse and its ancestors evolved provided no options for regular consumption of this form of rapidly available energy. So the nutritional paradox troubling other animals of the modern world often besets the horse as well. Horses can easily assimilate starch and sugar in small amounts, and even occasional high amounts. Fresh grass and grass hay average about 10 percent sugar and starch.

Table 10 is a study of Coastal Bermudagrass that illustrates key issues typical of all grasses. The first point demonstrated by the data in Table 10 is the higher protein in pasture (16 percent) compared to hay (10 percent). What this illustrates is that hay is harvested late in the plant's life when it is done growing. At this time, its metabolism is geared towards putting stored energy into seeds for the next generation or root storage for nutrition during approaching winter. Earlier in the plant's life, when grazed as pasture by horses, the plant is in growth mode, using captured energy promptly to make new plant tissue.

The next point shown in Table 10 is that starch plus sugar in mature hay averages more than 13 percent, while younger pasture averages seven percent or less. Besides a mature plant being higher in starch than a younger plant, there is a third important point. The range of starch content from the beginning to end of one cutting can vary over 35-fold. It can be as low as 0.25 percent in fresh pasture, or as high as

Table 10 Bermudagrass hay (100 percent dry matter) comparing two crop years and pasture vs hay; 950 hay and 25 pasture samples. Adapted from Dairy One Forage Analysis: http://www.dairyone.com/Forage/feedComp/main.

Year	Protein	Fiber	Starch			Sugar	Sugar + Starch
			Low	Average	High		
07 Hay	10.52	66.51	2.54	5.63	8.72	8.39	14.02
09 Hay	10.39	66.29	2.30	5.88	9.44	7.27	13.15
Average	10.45	66.40	2.42	5.75	9.08	7.83	13.58
07 Pasture	15.36	65.80	0.45	2.46	4.48	5.48	7.94
09 Pasture	17.85	77.28	0.25	1.25	2.20	4.75	6.00
Average	16.60	71.54	0.35	1.85	3.34	5.11	6.97

9.44 percent in mature hay. (These values are all on a 100 percent dry matter basis.) Even in mature hay, it can range from 2.3 percent to 9.44 percent, a four-fold increase. In a primordial setting, closely approximated by pasture, horses select young plants high in protein and low in starch and sugar, and in so doing take in a dry matter that is seven percent starch plus sugar, probably the optimum amount for the horse from an evolutionary standpoint.

A review of Table 6 in Chapter 3 will show that with the exception of honey, nothing in the world that suffices as nourishment for mammals contains soluble carbohydrate over about five percent, as fed. Table 8 highlights that grains are over 60 percent in all cases, so need to be fed cautiously. Hay (dry matter) can be 13 percent starch plus sugar, nearly twice as high as for fresh pasture, but within the range tolerated by healthy horses.

Evolved to fit the niche of a herbivore, it is possible for a horse to have a long and healthy life eating nothing but grass hay. Obviously, the quality of the hay is important, but even here, the horse can compensate for some loss of quality by eating more of the hay. This is the origin of the term hay belly, used to describe a horse that has an unthrifty appearance and a big belly. Forced to make do on poor hay, the horse eats more of it to try to meet its needs.

Regarding protein, grass hay will range from seven to 13 percent and average 10 percent. The reason for such variability is a function of the age of the plant at the time it is harvested, and the temperature and moisture while it is growing. A very young plant will be excellent nutrition, high in digestible energy and protein and low in fiber (and starch). However, the drawback is that there is not much dry matter in a stand of immature hay. A fully mature stand of hay will have significantly more tons of dry matter per acre than when it was young, but the disadvantage is that, on a percentage basis, the level of fiber will be much higher, and the protein much lower (See Figures 16 and 17).

The free ranging horse deals with this issue by selecting what it prefers from the entire offering of the pasture or prairie, and in so doing influences its nutritional intake quite beyond the average of all plants in the pasture. If you observe a horse grazing freely, you will notice that it is not an indiscriminate mowing of whatever happens to be next to its mouth. It is actually a very proactive selection process, with some plants considered, but passed over. The horse is innately an accomplished expert at forage selection.

The hay grower on the other hand brings no such selection to the harvesting of his hay crop. All plants are mowed at the same moment in time, and further, that moment in time is invariably late in the plant's life, even partly gone to seed in some cases. Though it is seldom considered in this light, the horse owner and the hay

METRIC TONS/HECTARE (1 hectare = 2.47 acre)

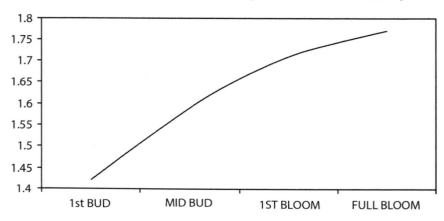

Figure 16 *Effect of plant age on yield of a hay crop.*

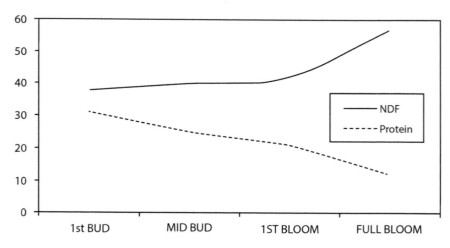

Figure 17 *Effect of age of plant on nutrient percent.*

grower are in conflicting positions, with the hay grower making the most money by selling more tons, optimized when the pasture is mature, and the horse owner in the market to buy quality nutrition, best when the plants are young.

A working compromise would be for the horse owner to agree to pay the hay grower a predetermined price (profit) per acre for his hay pasture, and then the farmer cuts the hay when the horse owner dictates. Few horsemen buy enough hay to even consider this solution. Some horse owners buy hay from one supplier, several weeks' supply at a time. Many horses are kept in a rented stall at a horse facility where hay is included in the monthly fee. Other horses are on farms where pasture is available in the summer, and they are hay fed in the winter. All these cases usually result in hay from one cutting, from one field, from one farm, and all one analysis. Thus, the horse owner feeds hay of the same analysis for many weeks, be it optimum or not.

Measures are called for to ensure quality hay, the most reliable of which is laboratory analysis. Commercial forage labs have preaddressed mailer packs for this purpose. This requires a special hay auger tool to properly sample hay bales. Farm supply catalogues offer these for sale, and the cost ($15 to $90) of a laboratory analysis depends on what nutrients you select for assay. When it is considered that hay is the predominant feed of a horse, and horse owners spend a great deal of money on hay, an analysis protocol is a worthwhile investment.

Horse owners talk about hay quality in terms of its protein content, which is not completely accurate, but it does tend to work. It is inaccurate because the overall digestibility of a hay is not predicted completely by its protein content. It is possible to have an adequate level of protein, but low digestibility. However, the reason protein content tends to be useful is because it has an acceptable measure of correlation with digestibility.

The major nutrients of concern regarding hay analysis are protein; higher protein indicates younger and more digestible hay, and lower neutral detergent fiber (NDF), or acid detergent fiber (ADF) and lignin. NDF and ADF are well correlated. The lower the fiber and lignin, the higher the digestibility of the hay. A grass hay that is above 70 percent NDF or more than eight percent lignin will be less digestible, and the horses will tell you as much by asking you when you feed it, "You got anything better?" and by going to it slowly, without enthusiasm, and rolling it around uneaten. Alfalfa is much appreciated by a horse, and most tolerate it well. A few horses get "hot" or hyperactive on alfalfa and others are seemingly allergic to it. These individuals are easily identified and their diets changed. It is possible to feed some horses on an all alfalfa diet, and they are happy horses indeed, but it is not necessary, and in most parts of the world, expensive.

Alfalfa will assay 18 to 26 percent protein, with the same arguments about digestibility pertaining as for grass hay. Alfalfa is best if the NDF is below 50 percent of the dry matter. Alfalfa as a crop is better adapted to cooler or drier climates. Usually a stand of alfalfa will last four or five years, and each year, it will tend to be a higher percentage of volunteer grass. These alfalfa/grass blends, when you can find them, can be ideal forages for horses.

Owners of horses with Cushings or diabetes are usually advised to feed a low starch diet. Cushing syndrome in horses (equine hyperadrenocorticism) is caused by a tumor of the pituitary gland, and is encountered more in older horses (over 15) though it can occur earlier. Technically, it is referred to as pars intermidia adenoma (PIA). Clinical signs can take years to develop, with long curly hair a common symptom. Definitive diagnosis requires specific blood tests as several symptoms of Cushings, such as laminitis and diabetes, can have different causes.

Feeding a low starch diet means avoiding grains, which are 60 to 80 percent soluble carbohydrate, and feeding low starch hay. Finding a low starch hay can be more challenging than one might think, as the intricacies of plant physiology can result in grass hay as high as 20 percent soluble carbohydrate. So many conditions of the plant environment can affect hay starch content, that the only reliable precaution is laboratory analysis. Starch is the form of energy storage in plants, performing the role of fat in mammals. Stored starch in the seed provides energy for growth until leaves can capture the energy of the sun via photosynthesis. Later in the season, leaves provide energy to be stored as starch in seeds to fuel the next generation.

Many environmental factors can alter a plant's starch level. For example, drought can speed up the accumulation of this starch, and its amount can be influenced by things as subtle as the rate of onset of the drought, the time of year, the geography, soil type and nutrient level, and especially the species of grass, whether cool season or warm season. Even very mature grass hay can be high in starch. If your horse must restrict soluble carbohydrate intake it is critical to assay grass hay before buying. As discussed above, mature hay can be four times the starch level as the same plant when immature – when it should be eaten by horses.

PROTEIN

The mature mare or gelding needs about 10 percent protein in the diet, which can all come from quality grass hay. Stallions actually have a slightly lower requirement because their higher testosterone metabolizes amino acids more efficiently. The concept of protein biologic value discussed in Chapter 2 also applies to the growing horse. Several scientific studies have shown that the growing horse is sensitive to protein quality, with weanlings fed milk protein growing faster than those fed soybean meal, which in turn grew faster than those fed cottonseed meal. It was shown that lysine was the most limiting amino acid, demonstrating the response of young horses to protein quality.

The mature horse is less affected by protein quality, for like all adults, the need for protein is less than when growing. The National Research Council's publication, *Nutrient Requirements of Horses 2007* is as scholarly and complete a treatment as we have available at this time, and is summarized in Table 15 in the Appendix. It reports that a protein level in the diet of 10.6 percent of the dry matter is adequate for mature horses of any sex, gestating mares of any trimester, and light or moderate working horses. Horses in heavy work are said to need 11.6 percent protein, and early lactation mares 13.2 percent. The highest protein requirement listed is weanlings at 14.5 percent. When you consider that quality grass hay can be 13 percent protein, and as pasture 18 percent, you can see that for nearly all horses, proper diet is little more than feeding quality grass hay. While this works in the wild, where innate behavior and feed selection have free play, most horse owners feel more confident providing some grain. There is no problem with this, if the amount is kept at less than 1.0 kg (2.2 lbs), the grain protein level is 14 to 16 percent and body condition and weight are properly monitored.

CARBOHYDRATE (GRAIN)

There are dozens of different grain type feeds that are used in horse products. Suffice it to say that most of us are at the mercy of the feed store and the formulas they have to offer. Some feed stores can procure single ingredients, such as beet pulp or rice bran. The first rule to bear in mind regarding any feed or grain is that too much of anything is not good. On the other hand, in proper dose, the horse can derive benefit from nearly all common feeds and grains. As discussed above, few horses need protein above 11 percent on a 100 percent dry matter basis. Grains and hays are usually about 10 percent moisture, so a feed tag that claims 12 percent protein, in the bag, is actually 13.3 percent protein on a 100 percent dry matter basis. Sweet feeds, meaning any grain type supplement product in a bag, are fed to adjust condition or body weight, or deliver micronutrients, and there is rarely any call for a horse grain supplement to be over 14 percent protein, as fed. Regarding weight, consider first the over-conditioned horse, a far too common body condition.

It is unfortunate that scales for weighing horses are so scarce, for it has been proven repeatedly that people are notoriously inept at estimating a horse's weight. An alternative is a tape measure, used around the girth just behind the front legs. These tapes estimate with fair accuracy, but even if they are not always correct, they will quite correctly reflect a relative change in one horse from one week to the next week. Even a piece of baling twine can serve as a measure in this way.

A girth measurement can be a good way to determine if progress is being made on a weight reduction program. In very overweight horses, the first sign of progress in weight reduction will actually be seen around the belly in front of the back legs. Few people with fat horses have the self-discipline to put their horses on a diet, which is sad, as fat horses are obviously compromised in doing all the things horses are noted for, and they are more prone to problems. Fat horses are the result of kind-hearted and well-meaning owners, but the kindest thing to do is apply a little self-discipline. Reduce their feed.

Book values on horse nutrition unavoidably speak in averages, ignoring the wide variation that is a reality in all of life science. While it may be true that the average mature horse working two hours a day, three days a week, can maintain body condition on grass hay alone, there are numerous exceptions. Some horses are "hard keepers" and need some grain supplementation even with this mild workload. One may ask how hard keepers maintain in the wild, when they eat the same grass hay. Recall that they have the advantage of selecting the choice plants and plant parts. More importantly, when fresh grass is cut and dried in the sun, it suffers some loss of digestibility, perhaps five to 10 percent, and diminishes still further over time in storage. If it is rained on before drying and baling, the loss of digestibility can be even more. Other horses are "easy keepers" and gain weight on grass hay alone, in some cases despite a mild workload. The trained eye of the keeper is the final jury in all such cases, and grain feeding inevitably comes down to using it prudently and administering it for effect.

The principle reason to feed grain is to deliver carbohydrate. Carbohydrate is a bit risky as a term because the way it is most often intended and its correct meaning are not in agreement. When people mention carbohydrate, they presume to mean sugar and starch, which is the underlying topic discussed in this section. But the term carbohydrate very correctly includes fiber. Cellulose, acted on by enzymes, breaks down to starch. The classification carbohydrate is actually correctly composed of the two sub groups, fiber and non-fiber carbohydrate, with the non-fiber fraction also referred to as soluble carbohydrate, mentioned so often in this book.

Soluble carbohydrate can be in the form of sugar, which everyone knows horses love. Other than an occasional treat, sugar as a routine feed ingredient is not a good idea for horses. It is quickly digested and elevates blood sugar efficiently, which is to say caloric needs are met easily, and subsequent hay intake, the feed that should predominate in the diet, leads to excess caloric intake.

Horse professionals the world over know that whole oats are a preferred grain for horses. One reason for this is that whole oats still include the oat hull, which is a slowly digested, fibrous outer covering, and acts in some ways just like hay. Oats are 42.4 percent neutral detergent fiber, compared to shell corn at 9.5 percent. The oat hull slows down digestion, but also slows down the rate of passage of the oat kernel. The slower rate of passage however, tends to increase total tract digestion, so the net effect of oats in the diet is to contribute the benefit of grain, without the drawbacks of grain.

The drawback of grain feeding is that it is easy to overdo it. Horses enjoy grain and, left to their own devices, will tend to eat more than they can properly digest at one time. This makes it quite essential to know the correct amount of grain to provide. If in doubt about how much grain is correct, feed less. Horses, like the pets we've discussed, are far more adapted to dealing with lack of energy than excess. If a mistake is made and too little feed is fed, it is easy to correct; just feed a little more tomorrow.

The problem of too much grain, besides the obvious danger of founder and colic, is that it tends to displace forage and hay, which are essential feeds the horse is adapted to use physiologically, nutritionally and behaviorally. Just as for monogastrics, high grain feeding poses a problem for the horse's metabolic machinery. Feeding over 11 lb of grain a day was associated with more than a four-fold increase in the chance of colic, and 22 lb or more with a six-fold increase in the chance of colic. Nothing in the evolutionary history of the horse or its ancestors prepared it for high soluble carbohydrate intake.

Imagine the starch introduced into the diet of a horse fed high amounts of grain, often 70 percent starch. Grain fed at 1 to 2 lb is usually well tolerated, and can be an ideal way to assure intake of micronutrients and supplements, and to shape behavior. Feeding grain above 2 lb is not necessary for any horse that maintains proper weight while performing the activities asked of it. Do not feed more than 2 lb of grain a day until it is well established that other options do not maintain weight and performance.

Like primates and pets, horses are adept at training people. They will leave hay uneaten, waiting for their keeper to provide more grain. When hay is uneaten, or poorly eaten, offer higher quality hay before feeding more grain. Most horses, once they have stopped eating grass hay, will readily eat additional alfalfa. More alfalfa is preferred to more grain, and costs less.

Perhaps you exercise your horses above average and are not convinced grain is of questionable value. Addressing just this topic, researchers at Cornell University did an eloquent experiment using exercised horses and 0, 2.2, 4.4, or 6.6 lb of ground corn fed in addition to a maintenance hay diet (Figure 18). Using a statistically powerful experimental design where each of the four horses was tested on each diet, they measured plasma glucose, insulin, lactate, free fatty acids (FFA) and muscle and liver glycogen. The horses were trained to walk, trot and gallop on a treadmill that could be changed from zero to two percent grade while they were running. Catheters were placed in the jugular vein and blood samples taken every 430 feet of the 2.75 miles. For the last mile the horses were galloping at 23.8 miles per hour on a two percent grade.

Heart rate at the end of the exercise averaged 206 beats per minute, intense but still sub maximum for a well-conditioned horse. These Standardbred horses (two mares and two geldings) averaged 975lb.

Standing next to one of these horses galloping full speed on a treadmill is absolutely awe inspiring. The noise is deafening as the hooves strike the treadmill in furious succession. It's exactly like standing relaxed within a meter of a racehorse every step of its race. In all the ways that man interacts with animals, nothing is more impressive. The horse's heart pumps a liter with every stroke, and at 206 beats per

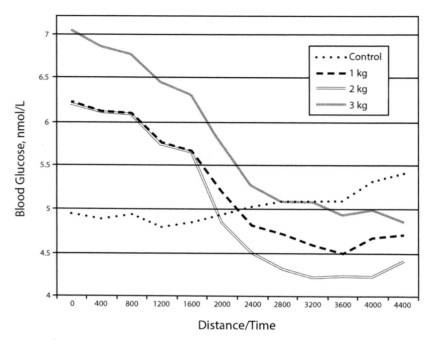

Figure 18 *Plasma glucose levels in exercising horses fed 0, 1, 2 or 3 kg of corn grain 2.5-3 hrs before exercise. Zero to 1600m, warmup at 6m/s; 1600 to 2400m, walk at 1.9 m/s; 2400 to 4400 m, gallop at 11m/s on 2 percent grade. Exercise did not reduce blood glucose (P < .05) if a horse was fed no grain.*

minute (over three beats per second!) it can fill a bathtub in one minute. Per unit of body weight, no animal exceeds the horse for power and sustained athleticism.

Figure 16 shows some of the data from the Cornell trial of Dr. Lawrence and her collaborators. Regardless of individual, sex, diet or time period, a horse finished the exercise with statistically higher blood glucose if fed hay alone without any grain. Any amount of grain resulted in a statistically lower blood glucose at the end of exercise compared to a diet of hay alone. Keep in mind that each horse was tested on each diet, in other words, they were their own control. This trial did not duplicate an endurance effort, but it was 2.75 miles in 15 minutes on a two percent grade (two meter foot in 100 feet) and was rigorous exercise most horse owners rarely achieve.

This research supports the point of view that horses do not benefit, and maybe even are harmed, by the feeding of constant excess soluble carbohydrate, just like other mammals. Related to this point, research has shown that corn, if cooked, is much more rapidly digested in the small intestine. Besides providing increased energy via the small intestine, this has the added advantage of lessening the grain that arrives to the cecum and large intestine. This is good, because grain in these organs is not digested, but fermented by the bacteria. Colic is mostly a mystery, truth be told, but one fact is established: colic incidence increases with increased grain feeding. Less grain feeding and cooking or extruding grain for horses would help.

FATS

Horses are able to accommodate diets that are up to 10 percent fat in most situations. The research literature reports successful trials using 15 percent vegetable oil. It appears that fat is easily digested by horses, with values in the literature of 93 to 95 percent digestibility for fat. The term fat means all plant fats and oils as well as other lipid compounds. Grass hay will tend to be about two to three percent fat, and as such is a true representative of the average fat intake of a horse on pasture. However, the modern horse is often trained and exercised intensely, and supplemental fat can help maintain body condition in some individuals.

Fat is over twice the caloric content of carbohydrate or protein, and a small addition of supplemental fat significantly increases caloric intake without triggering the insulin release caused by the carbohydrate of grains. It is the horse's evolutionary heritage to consume plant fats, and although animal fats can suffice to some extent as an energy source, it is recommended that fat supplemented for energy purposes be of plant origin. There are specific components of fat, such as linoleic acid and linolenic acid, which are more correctly viewed as micronutrients or nutraceuticals. Nutraceuticals are plant micronutrients with drug like effects. Caffeine, with its transitory impact as a stimulant, is an example of such a plant compound everyone is familiar with.

MAJOR MINERALS OF HORSE NUTRITION

An area of nutrition of concern to horsemen is calcium and phosphorus. A portion of horse owners are involved in raising baby horses to adulthood, and these people sometimes see developmental problems that the majority of horse owners are blissfully spared. As always, we must be prepared to admit that our breeding and selection pressures, in conjunction with premature workloads, can bring on problems. But this can also force us to learn better methods. To the extent that we have any insight about developmental bone problems, one common component encountered is excess dietary energy while growing.

For example, wobbler is a term given to young horses that have a stumbling gait, due to pinched nerves in their neck. The clinical term for this affliction is cervical vertebral malformation (CVM), which means basically that the spinal cord or more specifically one or more vertebrae, are not properly formed. One type of intervention to show measurable success was early identification, confinement and greatly reduced plane of nutrition. In other words, grow these individuals more slowly. The trick is to grow adequate or near normal skeletal frame, but retard tissue and muscle growth to the slowest possible without irreversible harm. The same type of problem, and cure, is seen in food agriculture animals where the rush to produce meat essentially overgrows young stock into bone and connective tissue problems.

In these insights we are reminded again how dealing with lack of nutrition is something nature is well prepared for. No species has learned to cope with prolonged excess nutrition.

The National Research Council publication recommends that the maintenance diet of a mature horse needs to provide 20g calcium and 14g phosphorus daily, with the stallions in breeding needing slightly more at 30 and 18g respectively. Note that calcium is always higher than phosphorus. Most grass hays, if not too old at harvest, meet these needs. Thirty-day-old orchard grass hay is 0.32 percent calcium and 0.20 percent phosphorus, but 40-day-old orchard grass is 0.26 percent calcium, which starts to be a little low, even for idle horses. During intense work, polo or race training for example, the requirement increases to 40g calcium and 29g phosphorus. Gestating mares, nursing mothers and weanlings can require more calcium than is available from poor quality grass hay. Peak lactation mares need 60g of calcium each day, and 38g of phosphorus. Four-month-old weaned youngsters need about 40g of calcium and 21g of phosphorus, with late lactation mares and six-month-olds needing less than these values.

Alfalfa and clover hays can provide much more calcium than this, as these plants are invariably over one percent calcium. But some phosphorus supplementation is indicated for gestating and lactating mares and growing stock. Most grains are high in phosphorus, such as oats at 0.38 percent. Otherwise, common additions to horse feeds are limestone at 38 percent calcium, and dicalcium phosphate which is 18 percent calcium and 21 percent phosphorus. These ingredients quickly increase the mineral content of a diet but the digestibility of the calcium and phosphorus of these sources is less than the endogenous calcium and phosphorus in hays and grains.

Other macro minerals are critical, the major ones being potassium, sodium, magnesium and sulfur. For potassium, magnesium and sulfur, the story is easily told in its basic terms. Just as for calcium and phosphorus, the native grasses alone provide a major portion of the needs, with modest amounts of supplemental grains filling in much of the remainder. In some cases, it is left to a grain supplement, fortified with minerals such as magnesium sulfate or potassium chloride, to provide the last portion of a requirement.

Sodium however, is a unique nutrient for the horse, as the horse is one creature that sweats profusely, and thereby needs free access to salt, especially if it is working in hot weather. Sodium is one mineral known for certain to drive a craving for salt if it is deficient. If salt blocks are freely available, a deficiency in horses is not likely.

Trace mineral is the term used for mineral nutrients required in very low levels, on the order of milligrams per kilogram of diet or parts per million. There are no known unique needs of the horse for any traditional trace minerals, covered in more detail for all companion animals in a later chapter.

VITAMINS

Chapter 10 discusses vitamins in more detail. I am providing a few comments specific to the horse here. Vitamins are divided into two categories: fat soluble and water soluble. The fat soluble vitamins are A, D, E and K. Carotene is fat soluble and referred to as provitamin A. It is advisable to supplement vitamin A. Although fresh forage contains high levels, few horses enjoy the luxury of year round pasture. Vitamin A is not expensive and is readily available in manufactured feeds. 15,000 IU of vitamin A per day is a prudent level of supplementation for mature idle horses, with horses in heavy exercise needing 22,500 IU, and 30,000 IU required by pregnant and lactating mares.

Vitamin D is likewise not expensive to supplement, with no risk of side effects at prudent levels. 3300 IU per day of vitamin D is recommended for all adult horses, with up to 5800 IU for two-year-olds in heavy exercise. It is doubtful that horses on a normal diet and exposed to any amount of sunlight will develop vitamin D deficiency.

Among other things, vitamin D is involved in calcium metabolism and the prevention of bone diseases such as rickets. Carotene, usually called beta-carotene (β-carotene), is abundant in fresh forage and probably not a dietary requirement if pasture is available. However, β-carotene is implicated in the reproductive process, quite apart from vitamin A, and mares to be bred without access to fresh pasture should be supplemented with β-carotene. Ovulation in mammals give rise to the corpus luteum, needed for pregnancy maintenance. Corpus luteum means yellow body in Latin, the yellow in this case from β-carotene. As for most vitamins, exact requirements are not determined. A suggested level for β-carotene is 200mg per breeding mare per day.

Vitamin E, as for vitamin A and D, is abundant in fresh forage, but tends to fade more quickly as hay dries in the sun, and more so as it ages in storage. The form of vitamin E in forage is fragile, specific to nature, and not easy to manufacture in standard feed industry systems. The commercial form of vitamin E is referred to as synthetic, and it is not as potent as the natural form found in fresh forage. It is possible to buy natural vitamin E, but it is in an oil base mixture (remember they are called fat soluble), has a short shelf life and it is expensive. There are biochemical alternatives that deliver most of the value of natural vitamin E without the fragile shelf life or inconvenience of administering oil. These are more economical than pure natural vitamin E but newer in the marketplace and not widely available. Evidence for the greater bioavailability of natural vitamin E in other species has been increasing in the scientific literature for the past decade, but only suspected for the horse. A recent publication finally verifies the greater bioavailability of natural vitamin E for the horse.

The best approach is to be sure to supplement adequate amounts of vitamin E, natural or synthetic. I suggest that the average adult horse receive 1000 IU of vitamin E in the synthetic form, or 300 IU in the natural form. It is almost impossible to overfeed vitamin E. Besides being of very low toxicity, no one could afford to do it, as vitamin E is much more expensive than vitamin A or D.

Vitamin K is a generic term for the antihemorrhagic factor in plants and intestinal bacteria. In all but the most unusual circumstances, horses receive adequate vitamin K activity from these two sources.

Water soluble vitamins are also called B-complex vitamins. The known water soluble vitamins of import for the horse are thiamin, riboflavin, niacin, pantothenic acid, pyridoxine (B6), biotin, folic acid and B12. With the exception of B12, the water soluble vitamins are usually supplied in adequate amounts in forage, or by microbial synthesis in the cecum and large intestine. Vitamin B12 is not produced by animals or higher plants so will not be adequate in hays and forages, but anaerobic bacteria with access to cobalt will produce B12. Therefore this issue is dealt with for the horse by supplementing cobalt in the trace mineral mix, usually on the order of 0.1ppm of diet dry matter.

There is growing evidence that biotin can be helpful in correcting poor hoof wall integrity or for hoof health. Details are far from complete for horses, but this vitamin is proven to be effective for hoof health in other species. For a biotin supplement to improve hoof health, it would need to be supplemented for several months as it takes six months for new hoof wall to grow from the top of the hoof to the ground.

There is no harm in supplementing B-complex vitamins to mature horses, but the prevailing opinion of experts in the field is that quality forage and balanced feed programs do not require B-complex augmentation in normal circumstances. For the growing horse, the brood mare or for those in intense training, it may prove one day that supplementation is indicated. For now, there is no harm in prudent addition of water soluble vitamins, but keep in mind that it is not established it is doing any measurable good for most horses. Table 15 in the Appendix lists the few vitamin and trace mineral recommendations the experts have put forth.

SUPPLEMENTS

Because of the eloquent adaptability perfected in mammals by evolution, a wrong diet is never a sudden crisis. Aware that nutrition may be sub-optimal yet not readily apparent, many horse owners are inclined to consider supplements. The existence of some brightly labeled jug on a store shelf is not proof your horse is deficient in what is in that jug. There are infinite supplement products offered for the horse owner to ponder, with credibility ranging from dubious to honest good deals.

Begin the analysis of your horse's nutrition program from the solid premise that the horse is a remarkable survival machine, and when supplied with quality forage and a professional, common sense grain supplement, it will thrive just fine. If you are offering quality forage and a professional grain supplement, and yet have what appear to be nutrition problems, look first to environment and behavior for the cause. If your horse is confined on concrete or dirt, lonely, bored or desperate for physical activity, no amount of snake oil or enzyme CoQ (known as CoQ10), will cure his hives.

Regarding probiotics for horses, this topic, as more fully discussed in Chapter 7, is applicable to the horse and could be inserted here in its entirety. A lot of probiotic use is based on inertia or momentum, word of mouth or just plain "always done it" mentality. Though the benefits may be nonexistent, elusive or hard to demonstrate, harmful effects (other than expense, which can be significant) are rare and invariably fleeting. Fortunately, this area of horse nutrition is improving, and there are sound reasons to consider using good probiotics. Research in 2008 showed a beneficial effect of FOS (fructooligosaccharide) for horses, which is technically a prebiotic, but logical in that FOS is a common component of plants that horses graze.

The topic of probiotics for horses reduces to the same point as many other horse nutrition issues. There is not a lot of scientific literature properly proving efficacy for probiotics or supplements in horses. Such validation, though sparse, is growing and lack of proof does not mean a product is ineffective. Many horse professionals swear by their favorite coat conditioner, and it is one category where subjective judgment can suffice. A healthy coat with shine is easy to discern from a poor coat, especially if over several months and absent in unsupplemented horses on the same regimen.

There are effective products to consider, but it is most difficult for the horse owner to discern valuable products from worthless label dressing. The best insurance is to buy from suppliers who welcome your inquiry and curiosity, and who consider expert technical answers a fundamental ingredient of their feed products.

REFERENCES

drought can speed up the accumulation of starch... Watts, KA. 2009. *Carbohydrates in forage: What is a safe grass? In Advances in Equine Nutrition IV. Ed: JD Pagan, Nottingham University Press. UK. p29.*

the growing horse is sensitive to protein quality... NRC, 2007 (National Research Council). *Nutrient Requirements of Horses. 6th Revised ed. The National Academies Press, 500 Fifth Street, NW. Washington, DC 2001.*

lysine the most limiting amino acid... Ott, EA., and J Kivipelto. 2002. *Growth and development of yearling horses fed either alfalfa or Coastal Bermudagrass hay and a concentrate formulated for bermudagrass hay. J. Equine Vet. Sci. 22:311-319)*

scholarly and complete... NRC, 2007 (National Research Council). *Nutrient Requirements of Horses. 6th Revised ed. The National Academies Press, 500 Fifth Street, NW. Washington, DC 2001.*

four fold increase in chance of colic... Tinker, MK, NA White, P Lessard, CD Thatcher, KD Pelzer, DK CArmet. 1997. *Prospective study of equine colic risk factors. Equine Vet. J. 29:454-458.*

Researchers at Cornell University... Lawrence, L., L. Soderholm, A Roberts, J Williams, H Hintz. 1993. *Feeding status affects glucose metabolism in exercising horses. J. Nutr. 123:2152-2157.*

*if cooked, corn is much more rapidly digested...*Meyer, H., S Radicke, E Kienzle, S Wilks, D Kleffken. 1993. *Investigations on preileal digestion of oats, corn and barley starch in relation to grain processing. In: Proceedings of the 13th Equine Nutrition and Physiology Symposium. Pp 92-97. Florida.*

successful trials using 15 percent vegetable oil... Holland, JL., DS Kronfeld, GA Rich, KA Kline, JP Fontenot, TN Meacham, PA Harris. 1998. *Acceptance of fat and lecithin containing diets by horses. Appl. Anim. Behav. Sci. 56:91-96.*

93-95 percent digestibility for fat... Kronfeld, DS., JL Holland, GA Rich, SE Custalow, JP Fontenot, TN Meacham, DJ Sklan, PA Harris. 2004. *Fat digestibility in Equus caballus follows first-order kinetics. 2004. J. Anim. Sci. 82:1773-1780.*

measureable success with CMV... Foreman, JH. 2005. *Losing control: Nutrition-related diseases of the central nervous system. In Advances in Equine Nutrition III. JD Pagan, ed. Nottingham University press. Nottingham. UK.*

greater bioavailability of Natural Vitamin E... Pusterla, N., B. Puschner, S. Steidl, J. Collier, E. Kane, RL Stuart. 2010. *Vet Record. α-tocopherol concentration in equine serum cerebrospinal fluid after vitamin E supplement. 166:12, 366-368. doi:10.1136/vr.b4802.*

Effective for hoof health in other species... Bergsten, C., PR Greenough, JM Gay, WM Seymour, CC Gay. 2003. Effect of biotin supplementation on performance and claw lesions on a commercial dairy farm. *J. Dairy Sci.* 86:3953-3962.

Beneficial effect of FOS for horses... Respondek, F., AG Goachet and V Julliand. 2008. Effect of dietary short-chain fructooligosaccharides on intestinal microflora of horses subject to a sudden change of diet. *J. Anim. Sci.* 86:316-323.

9

CAT NUTRITION:
PARADOX AT ITS BEST

The cat is a carnivore. It does not consume plants directly except on rare occasions. By definition, carnivore means the cat eats predominantly other animals. This usually is translated into "meat eater" in the mind of the average person, and as such is not correct. Pure muscle meat is woeful nutrition.

When a carnivore harvests its prey, far more than just the muscle meat is consumed. If allowed enough time at a kill, a pride of lions will consume everything, meaning all the bones and cartilage, intestines and contents, hide, hair and hooves. In so doing, many tissues and nutrients besides meat are consumed. Bones provide minerals otherwise very deficient in meat. Internal organs can be quite rich in vitamins not prevalent in muscle meat. Invariably the prey is a herbivore, and its intestinal contents are not just plant material, but a careful selection of the more nutritious plants parts, and high in concentration of antioxidants and other micronutrients.

Figure 19 illustrates the digestive anatomy of the cat. Similar to the ferret, mink and other carnivorous leaning species of low fiber intake, the anatomy is simplistic, lacking any fermentation compartments. The small intestine in the domestic cat is three feet long with faster rate of passage compared to herbivores. The lower fiber, and easier digestion of the standard carnivore diet allows this faster rate of passage.

The feeding frequency of a true carnivore is far more episodic than the omnivore or herbivore. Most zoos feed their carnivores once each day, but have one day a week when no food is provided or only bones. Management of large felids in this way is predicated on the observable fact that in the wild they often go for a day or two without harvesting any prey. People who own domestic cats know that there can be days when their daily feeding is of little interest to them.

There are differences in protein metabolism for cats compared to dogs. Compared to the dog, the cat is far less capable of up and down regulation of the enzymes involved in amino acid breakdown. What this means is that if a dog's protein intake suffers, it is able to down regulate the enzymes that metabolize amino acids, and be less compromised by a protein deficient diet. The dog, in turn, is less capable of

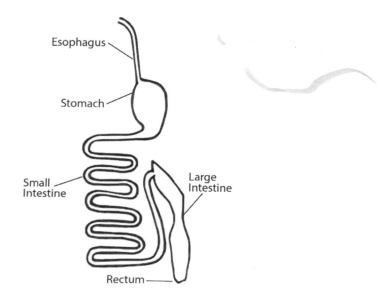

Figure 19 Digestive anatomy of the domestic cat.

this regulation than the rat. The fading of these enzymes for protein breakdown (for energy use, for example) takes one to five days in the dog, and once changed, leaves the dog unable to efficiently use a high protein diet until the enzymes are ramped up again.

For the cat, these enzymes are always at their peak efficiency. So the cat makes a tradeoff. Gambling that it will always be able to harvest a high protein meal, it forsakes the option of being able to maintain nitrogen balance on a low protein meal. The additional advantage of this for the cat is that if it has not eaten for five days due to bad luck in hunting, its enzymes are fully prepared to make efficient use of the high protein meal when it does happen. Not so for the dog. If after five days of fasting it captures a bird or squirrel or finds some quail eggs, it will not derive the same sustenance from the meal as the cat.

What this really highlights is the incredible capability of the cat as a predator. Evolution would not have permitted the cat to survive as a species using its carnivorous food strategy if it was not very successful. Said another way, the ability to down regulate protein breakdown enzymes would not have slipped into dormancy in the cat if it were not such a proficient and lethal hunter.

The cat is different in other ways as well. The ability to synthesize the amino acid taurine is nearly absent in carnivores, so unlike the dog, the cat requires taurine in its diet. But here again, it would appear evolution knew what it was doing. Taurine is one of the most abundant free (not used in protein) amino acids in mammals, being most prevalent in brain, heart and skeletal muscle. As such, it is a routine component of a carnivore's diet, and lack of capability for its synthesis is of little concern.

However, cats fed a vegetarian diet, or a dog food, will soon show taurine deficiency symptoms, which, left untreated, lead to blindness and heart failure. Fed a diet of adequate protein quality and amount, taurine deficiency is never seen in the cat. Marketers that tout their product contains taurine, implying those who don't are inferior, obscure the fact that if their diet matched the carnivores genetic heritage, no taurine addition would be needed.

Table 13 (Appendix page 173) shows nutrient requirements of the cat for reproduction and maintenance of adults, according to the National Research Council (NRC 2006). Any quality commercial cat food will meet these requirements. But there is an aspect of feline nutrition wholly ignored by this table. You will note there is no listing for carbohydrate. This is the very same principle that we have been discussing for the dog, horse and man. The cat is not only ill-equipped to deal with constant high soluble carbohydrate intake, it is the least prepared of any companion animal.

Table 11, summarized from foods of Table 6 in Chapter 3, is a list of the soluble carbohydrate content of general classes of food types in the primordial world.

Table 11 *Soluble Carbohydrate in foods (%, as fed)*

Food	Soluble Carbohydrate Content (%)
Meat & fish	1
Nuts	1-2
Grass sprouts	2-5
Insects	1
Fruits	6-8
Milk	3
Vegetables	4
Dry cat food	35-45

A carnivore's prey, including the herbaceous intestinal contents, is a very low source of soluble carbohydrate. Meat is one percent carbohydrate, mainly in the form of glycogen. Prey animal intestinal content will perhaps average four to five percent. A dry expanded cat food, to manufacture correctly, must be at least 35 to 45 percent soluble carbohydrate. This means a cat fed exclusively a dry kibble diet is consuming 10 to 20 times the level of soluble carbohydrate intended by evolution. While the cat can digest such a diet, just as we can occasionally eat sugar, a constant diet of the composition of dry kibble cat food (35 to 45 percent starch plus sugar) will lead to suboptimal nutrition and many subtle collateral problems, principal among them obesity and metabolic syndrome (diabetes). There is no proof of this to be found in the scientific literature on the cat. This should not surprise us. For years, reputable scientists have been saying that excess soluble carbohydrate is a problem, and few take notice. I remind you of the teaching of Dr. Atkins: that weight reduction in humans is easiest to achieve on a diet of high fat and protein and low carbohydrate, which was once again proven in the peer reviewed scientific literature in 2008.

If this is true for an omnivore who is designed to encounter soluble carbohydrate only on occasion, would it not hold true even more so for an obligate carnivore that rarely consumes any soluble carbohydrate? There may not be proof of this in the scientific literature on the cat, but there is research in the literature supporting this hypothesis.

The dog, like other omnivores, makes glucose (referred to as gluconeogenesis) principally after a meal. The cat, in contrast, is always in a state of gluconeogenesis, always making sugar, a strategy typical of a species not accustomed to ingesting periodic loads of glucose or soluble carbohydrates. Cats take longer than dogs to clear a dietary load of glucose and suffer galactosemia and galacotosuria if fed diets containing 39 percent galactose.

There is a liver enzyme in other species called glucokinase that responds to diet and blood levels of glucose, but in the cat this enzyme is diminished and likely leads to lower rates of glucose utilization. One researcher found no sucrase or lactase in pancreatic tissue of the cat. Another reported glucosuria (blood sugar spilling into the urine) in cats fed a diet of 25 percent glucose.

To the extent that experts are willing to estimate a safe upper limit for soluble carbohydrate for cats, it is three to ten times higher for the dog than the cat. These NRC authors also state that the extent to which carbohydrates are digested by the cat is controversial and even though cats may absorb dietary carbohydrates well, the rate of utilization of the resulting glucose likely is much less efficient.

CANNED DIETS

From the forgoing, it should be evident that dry kibble diets for cats provide more soluble carbohydrate than they require and more than is in the best interest of their health. Canned cat foods are more prevalent than canned dog foods. Being smaller than dogs, cats cost less to maintain because they eat smaller meals. Consequently, cat owners are more inclined to spend the higher price for food of the canned variety. Canned diets are more palatable to the cat, notorious for being finicky eaters.

The good news is that it is possible to make canned cat food without soluble carbohydrate, and in this regard, I recommend canned cat foods over dry kibble. Even if canned cat food is not possible as an entire diet, to the extent that it can be fed as a partial replacement for dry kibble, it will lessen the soluble carbohydrate your cat is consuming. Care must be exercised to not provide more canned cat food in addition to the standard amount of dry food, as this will promote obesity. However, most cats with access to both canned and dry food will voluntarily reduce their dry food intake as more canned food is provided. However, tartar buildup on the gums happens more readily in cats fed canned food.

RAW DIETS

There is one drawback to canned cat foods, the same one mentioned previously for canned dog foods. They are sterile by design and by definition. One meal devoid of any bacteria or molds, of course, is not a problem. But a lifetime of eating sterile food may not be in the cat's best interest nutritionally.

I've alluded to the common image seen in travel brochures of a leopard in a tree with its prey draped over a limb. The leopard retreated to this lofty perch to avoid the harassment of those who would relieve him of his dinner, and in so doing, may have dragged the half eaten carcass across many yards of African dirt. And in the climes where leopards reign, insects and flies are abundant, as is intense sunshine, all adding to the bacterial load of any meal.

Wild carnivores never eat sterile food and are well equipped to deal with bacteria. We have all seen the feral cat making a meal of the chicken carcass it found in the garbage. His life may not be what cat lovers envision for their cat, but it is often better nutritionally. An ideal solution for feeding a cat is to feed a commercially prepared raw diet. Be aware however, that raw diets require prudence and common sense regarding thawing and shelf life. They can be vectors for pathogens to get into the home, which is a major preoccupation for regulatory people.

Raw diets are becoming more available as entrepreneurs cater to the growing demand in the market. In most cases, raw diets are available in fresh and frozen form. Raw cat foods, either fresh or frozen, are lower in soluble carbohydrate, are not sterile and do not suffer the denaturing of native enzymes caused by the heat of canning or extrusion. This overcomes the biggest drawbacks of extruded and canned foods.

It may not be feasible to completely forsake dry extruded food for your cats, and to feed all fresh or frozen, but even if it partially replaces dry kibble, your cat's nutrition will be improved. Perhaps you can consider having three types of food for your cats: some kibble, some canned and some raw.

REFERENCES

the cat is far less capable of up and down regulation... Rogers, QR., JG Morris, RA Freeland. 1997. *Lack of hepatic enzymatic adaptation to low and high levels of dietary protein in the adult cat. Enzymes 22:348-356; and...* Tews, JK., QR Rogers, JG Morris, AE Harper. 1984. *Effect of dietary protein and GABA on food intake, growth and tissue metabolism of the cat. Physiol. Behav. 23:301-308.*

the dog less capable than the rat... Morris, JG., QR Rogers, JA O'Donnell. 2004. *Hepatic enzyme activity of puppies given adequate or high protein diets. Comp. Cont. Educ. Pract. Vet. 24:71 (absrt.).*

untreated taurine deficiency leads to blindness... NRC. 2006. *National Research Council. Nutrient Requirements of dogs and cats. The National Academies Press. 500 Fifth Street, N.W. Washington, D.C. 20001.*

teachings of Atkins... Atkins, RC. 2002. *Dr. Atkins' New Diet Revolution. M. Evans and Co., Inc. New York, NY. 10017.*

once again proven in the scientific literature... Shai, RD., D. Schwarzfuchs, Y Henkin, et al. 2008. *Weight loss with a low-carbohydrate, Mediterranean, or low-fat diet. N. Eng. J. Med. 359:229-241. (Subsequent correction: N. Eng. J. Med. 2008. 359(20):2169.)*

the cat is always in a state of gluconeogenesis... Kienzle, E. 1993a. *Carbohydrate metabolism in the cat. 2. Digestion of starch. J. Anim. Physiol. Anim. Nutr.69:102-114; and* Kienzle, E. 1993b. *Carbohydrate metabolism in the cat. 3. Digestion of sugars. J. Anim. Physiol. Anim. Nutr. 69:203-210.*

cats take longer than dogs to clear a load of glucose... Kienzle, E. 1994. *Blood sugar levels and renal sugar excretion after the intake of high carbohydrate diets in cats. J. Nutr. 124:2563S-2567S.*

leads to lower rates of glucose utilization... Ballard, FJ. 1965. *Glucose utilization in the mammalian liver. Comp. Biochem. Physiol. 14:437-443.*

found no sucrose or lactase in pancrease... Kienzle, E. 1993. *Carbohydrate metabolism in the cat. 4. Activity of maltase, isomaltase, sucrase and lactase in the gastrointestinal tract in relation to age and diet. J. Anim. Physiol. Anim. Nutr. 70:89-96.*

another reported glucosuria... Drochner, W., and S Muller-Schlosser. 1980. *Digestibility and tolerance of various sugars in cats. in Nutrition of the Dog and the Cat. Pg 101-111. RS Anderson, ed., London: Pergamon press.*

*limit for soluble carbohydrate for cats...*NRC. 2006. *National Research Council. Nutrient Requirements of dogs and cats. The National Academies Press. 500 Fifth Street, N.W. Washington, D.C. 20001. Tables 4-9, pages 73; controversial, page 55; use rate, page 52*

10

VITAMINS AND NUTRACEUTICALS

I t is not obvious what vitamins are doing when they do it. Lack of energy in a diet soon presents itself to the consciousness in telling ways, in hours in some cases. Lack of a vitamin takes much longer to become evident. Even while the lack of a particular vitamin is growing, perhaps as compromised skin health, it is not necessarily evident or a noticeable handicap in day-to-day life. Of course this is part of the grand design that enables mammals to endure temporary lack. Some vitamins are stored in different parts of the body such as in the liver or fatty tissue. Earlier I mentioned that vitamin A is stored in the liver. This is such an efficient process that seal liver is toxic and polar bears won't eat it. When a polar bear harvests a meal of ringed seal, all that can be found afterwards in the big patch of bloody snow is a seal liver. It is estimated that a human stores enough vitamin A in the liver to go many months without any dietary intake.

Vitamins are essential for life, meaning creatures can't make them for themselves and must have them provided across the gut wall, or in the case of vitamin D, promoted by sunshine on the skin. The layperson tends to think that everyone should have every vitamin supplemented in their diet on a regular basis, daily if not weekly, in well defined minimal amounts. This thinking extends by default to pets. There are many authoritative tables listing the daily recommended amounts for not only humans but just about every animal, poultry and even fish. Table 13 for cats, Table 14 for dogs and Table 15 for horses, all in the Appendix, show vitamin and trace mineral requirements.

The conventional point of view generally accepted by animal nutritionists is that adult ruminants do not need B vitamins in their diet. Their paunch is full of live bacteria that produce the needed B vitamins absorbed by the host animal further down the digestive tract. Curiously, this conventional outlook about herbivores is not applied to monogastrics, ignoring some perfectly evident facts. How do all the monogastric mammals in the wild survive without succumbing to vitamin deficiency? They never see the first vitamin pill or supplement, yet reproduce and enjoy healthy, full lives.

For that matter, how did any species survive for millions of years to the present without vitamin supplements? And what of the billions of bacteria in the gut of all mammals, not just ruminants? Is it possible that in a healthy monogastric these bacteria produce vitamins, absorbed by their host? Many people take vitamins, but far more do not, and seem to live healthy lives.

In his book Good Calories, Bad Calories, Taubes points out that early researchers discovering and proving vitamin needs found that deficiency symptoms could be induced in test animals by feeding a diet high in refined grains and sugar. This does not negate this foundation work or that vitamins are essential and required. But, it does beg the question: If a diet low in refined grains and sugar is fed, is supplementation still required? Is supplementation needed for all diets? Is it possible that vitamin requirements could be satisfied without supplements by some diets, or by less cooking and heat damage, or by friendly bacteria that thrive in the gut of a properly fed animal?

Dingoes, coyotes, wolves, tigers and lions survive in the wild without vitamin supplements. If our understanding of vitamin requirements is correct, these wild creatures are meeting their needs some way other than supplementation. Either that, or our understanding of an animal's vitamin needs is not correct. The greater probability is our current understanding of an animal's vitamin needs is well informed and correct more often than not. But the nutrition profession, as well as the lay consumer, needs to be more open to the possibility that animals can meet their vitamin needs by means other than supplementation – that diets needing supplementation to correct vitamin deficiency may be wrong diets.

I offer the following for your consideration: A properly balanced diet, not altered by heating or processing, does two things: it provides vitamins and enzymes from the food eaten in an un-denatured form (not damaged by heating), and promotes the growth of friendly bacteria that synthesize vitamins absorbed by the host. Another part of this hypothesis would be that high soluble carbohydrate diets cause lower vitamin absorption. A probable mechanism for this would be altered microbial growth, either by promoting the wrong bacteria, or hindering beneficial bacteria, or both.

As explained, a singular feature of a wild diet is low levels of soluble carbohydrate. There is strong evidence that high soluble carbohydrate diets increase the need for at least one vitamin. In a line of reasoning documented by Taubes, it is pointed out that diabetics and those suffering metabolic syndrome have significantly lower circulating levels of vitamin C. Glucose and vitamin C, being similar in shape, compete for the same absorption sites for transport into the cell and because glucose dominates in this process, it effectively regulates how much vitamin C gets into the cell. Infusing test subjects with glucose has been shown to cause a drop in blood levels of vitamin C.

Conventional wisdom is still rooted in the mentality of the era when vitamins were being discovered in the 1920s and '30s. The scientific process guided investigators to produce a deficiency in animals and then supplement candidate vitamin compounds to learn which reversed the symptom. This approach was entrenched with the well known history of scurvy in seamen, and how it could be prevented and cured with citrus fruit. Hundreds of years after citrus was recognized as curing scurvy, it was discovered the active component was ascorbic acid, vitamin C. Early investigations showed that beriberi, a vitamin deficiency encountered when polished rice predominated in a diet, could be reversed by adding rice hulls – or prevented in the first place by eating whole grain rice. It was subsequently learned the active ingredient in rice hulls was thiamin (vitamin B1). When vitamin A reversed night blindness in an animal, it was concluded, logically, that lack of vitamin A could cause night blindness. To also use this evidence as proof that everyone needed vitamin A in all diets at all times was not a conclusion sustained by the evidence.

In addition to the vitamin content of the diet, the preparation and composition of the diet used to produce the deficiency can play a critical role. In 2005 Liu assembled a provocative set of data using the US Department of Agriculture's web site for food composition (http://www.nal.usda.fnic). Table 12 shows the nutrient loss in whole wheat after it is refined into unenriched white flour.

Table 12 *Nutrients remaining in whole wheat after refining into unenriched white flour*

Nutrient	Percent remaining
Vitamin E	5
B6	13
Magnesium	15
Manganese	18
Riboflavin	19
Niacin	20
Fiber	22
Zinc	24
Potassium	26
Thiamin	27
Iron	30
Phosphorus	31
Copper	38

Nutrient	Percent remaining
Sodium	40
Pantothenate	43
Calcium	44
Selenium	44
Fat	52
B12	59
Folate	59
Protein	75
Energy	107

Given the fragility of many vitamins in the presence of heat or boiling water, the further erosion of the nutrition of white flour upon baking into bread adds new meaning to the term "empty calories." There is a fullness of nutrition to ripe fruits and vegetables consumed on the spot, without heat damage. But the modern food procurement system can't be expected to provide fresh raw food to everyone. Seven billion people simply can't subsist as hunter-gatherers on just one planet earth. At least not the way we are set up today. We can do better, and movement is afoot to nudge us in that direction. Meanwhile, the evidence is compelling that Western man has altered his environment outside the comfort zone of his genetic inheritance and that of his companion animals. Creative solutions are needed.

VITAMINS

Because vitamin C is well known, absence of its discussion would be conspicuous, so even though dogs, cats and horses don't require vitamin C in their diet, a brief look at its function is provided. Ascorbic acid (vitamin C) is a needed vitamin for humans, great apes and, curiously, guinea pigs. Some snakes, birds and fruit eating bats also need vitamin C in their diet. The animals we are discussing – the dog, cat and horse – can all make vitamin C for themselves from glucose.

Mentioned before, it has recently been discovered with the human genome elucidation, that humans possess all the DNA to make their own vitamin C. However, the last enzymatic step is turned off by another gene. Fruit eating bats may give us a clue as to why some species require vitamin C. One can surmise that a bat eating predominantly fresh fruit would consume a good measure of vitamin C. Perhaps a long ago chance mutation (actually, all mutations are chance) that shut off the metabolic machinery of a redundant pathway – redundant because vitamin C was already plentiful in the diet – saved energy and gave a survival advantage. Glucose is used to make vitamin C. It is possible that the ancient diet of humans and great apes provided adequate vitamin C, and a mutation shutting down the pathway saved some energy (and glucose) and caused no harm due to the constant vitamin C in the diet. What today is viewed as a handicap – needing vitamin C in the diet – was possibly an advantage in the primordial setting.

Ascorbic acid functions as a catalyst in many reactions of the body and as a cofactor in the synthesis of several hormones. It is required to make collagen, the major structural protein of animals. Deficiency symptoms include delayed wound healing and capillary fragility and bleeding. A common affliction of seamen with scurvy was bleeding gums. Perhaps the best known role of vitamin C is to act as a free radical scavenger, mopping up the exhaust fumes of metabolism itself, oxygen's reactive byproducts, not to mention the ravages of the environment such as sun damage (a form of radiation).

Momentarily, we will consider how the species of our concern differ from each other, or otherwise are noteworthy regarding vitamins and other micronutrients. First, here is a list of each vitamin and a brief summary of its main metabolic function.

Vitamin A: Dissolves in fat but not water so is called fat soluble. Needed for growth, vision, cellular differentiation (therefore critical in the developing fetus) and immune function. Derived from carotenoids of plants such as β-carotene. Cod liver oil and butter are good sources.

Vitamin D: Fat soluble. Required for proper bone structure as it plays a role in the regulation of calcium as well as phosphorus. In turn, calcium is required for many critical functions including muscle contraction, blood clotting and nerve signals. Fish oil is a good source. Cats and probably dogs gain no advantage from sunshine so must have this vitamin provided in the diet. Some animals can make use of the precursor form of vitamin D in the diet, but the common commercial form of vitamin D works for all species. Vitamin D is enjoying a rebirth of interest as its role in other important aspects of metabolism (such as cancer) is investigated.

Vitamin E: Fat soluble. Antioxidant and free radical scavenger preventing oxidative damage of lipid membranes. Can work in synergy with vitamin C. Common in plant oils. Hemolytic anemia (ruptured red blood cells) is a common deficiency symptom. Depending on the arrangement of its atoms, vitamin E can be structured in one of eight different ways. Vitamin E made synthetically contains all eight forms, but nature only deals in one of the eight forms. This is one place where health food advocates have a point. Natural vitamin E is better, two to three times so, but it also is more expensive. Both natural and synthetic vitamin E are fragile molecules, quickly degrading in time, so they are always protected by a process called esterification with the attachment of an acetate molecule. This lowers bioavailability to some extent, but greatly improves shelf life, a trade off everyone acknowledges is worthwhile.

Vitamin K: Fat soluble. Common in plants such as spinach, broccoli and tomatoes and also high in liver. Needed for normal blood clotting. Many species meet their total needs by intestinal synthesis of bacteria.

Thiamin (Vitamin B1): Dissolves in water, thus called water soluble, as are all that follow; also called the B vitamins due to the arbitrary labels used in the pioneering days of vitamin discovery. Thiamin occurs widely in both plants and animals in modest amounts and is found in higher concentrations in wheat germ, liver and kidney, yeast and legume seeds. Some plants (e.g. soybeans) contain an enzyme that destroys thiamin. Cooking the plant destroys this enzyme. Critical functions of thiamin involve energy and carbohydrate metabolism. Acute deficiency involves the heart and nervous system. Chronic lack affects the myocardium and peripheral nerves.

Riboflavin (Vitamin B2): Animal products, including milk, are good sources of riboflavin, while plants and grains are poor sources. Riboflavin is part of the coenzyme called FAD (flavin adenine dinucleotide) indispensable to energy metabolism. It also is essential in regeneration of scavenger molecules that are damaged in their role as police for lipid peroxides.

Pyridoxine (Vitamin B6): Over a hundred enzymatic reactions are known to use pyridoxal-5'-phosphate (PLP), the active form of the vitamin. Because of its importance in so many reactions, including with the vitamin niacin, pyridoxine affects glucose production, red blood cell function, nervous system function and immune response. Found in almost all foods, B6 is more abundant in egg, meat, fish, spinach, carrots, walnuts and wheat germ. A fragile vitamin, cooking and processing can deplete it. The commercial form used and shown on food labels is pyridoxine hydrochloride (HCL).

Niacin: Part of the coenzyme nicotinamide-adenine dinucleotide (NAD), a cofactor in many critical reactions. Cures pellagra in humans on a high corn diet, and black tongue in dogs. The practice in Mexico is to pre-treat corn by soaking in cold lime water which releases the niacin for absorption. Fairly common in plant and animal foods, it too can be a delicate nutrient. Boiling in water can destroy it.

Pantothenate: An indispensable part of coenzyme A, a central molecule in metabolism. It could be argued no molecule is more central. Found in a wide variety of foods: beef, pork, milk, eggs, saltwater fish, whole wheat, beans and fresh fruit. Processing and cooking can lower bioavailable levels.

Folate: The various forms of folate are cofactors in the metabolism of amino acids and nucleotides, and one carbon unit disposal. Folate's more recent notoriety has been due to its role in preventing neural tube defects in newborns, hence it is widely recommended for pregnant women. Found in many foods, good sources are animal liver, whole wheat, green leafy vegetables and brewer's yeast.

Vitamin B12 (Cobalamin): This vitamin is unique because it is only made by microorganisms. All animals, regardless of how they obtain B12 either get it directly from microbes or from something that does. The mineral cobalt is at the center of this molecule, so it may be that cobalt provided to an active gut microflora will obviate the need for consuming cobalamin. Plants and all their parts are devoid of B12. The only dietary source is animal foods. Rich sources are animal liver and kidneys, milk and cheese, and several sea foods. Its role in blood formation is well known; anemia is a classic deficiency symptom.

Biotin: Discovered in 1927, four enzymes are known to require biotin as cofactors. Dietary biotin is absorbed at 25 to 60 percent and the liver appears to store it well. Dietary lack will evidence like many vitamins as poor hair coat and skin infections. Another sign of deficiency is malformed newborns. Firm recommendations for dietary intake are not available for all species, but .03 milligrams per day are recommended for adult people. Biotin is widely found in natural foods and relatively rich in egg yolk, liver and some vegetables. As mentioned, there is evidence biotin plays an important role in hoof health and skin integrity, but can require up to six months for its effect to extend from the top growing part of a hoof to the ground.

NUTRACEUTICALS

There is a class of nutrients that fall into a category called nutraceuticals. The defining feature of these is they are included in a diet in miniscule amounts, like vitamins or trace minerals, are beneficial in their effect, but are not necessarily essential for life. In a bygone era, they might have been classed as vitamins, but our hubris being such as it is, the category of vitamin is not accepting any new candidates.

Some have argued this class of nutrients be called nutricines, as nutraceuticals is a term that misleads in that it aligns with pharmaceutical, and intervention to ameliorate a pathology. Nutraceuticals don't fix a broken metabolism, they help a functioning one run better. An example is coenzyme Q, referred to popularly as CoQ or CoQ10. Also known as ubiquinone, as it is found in so many biological systems, the 10 reflects a unique aspect of its molecular structure. One of its main functions is to participate in an electron shift with cytochrome C, the enzyme system found in all biology. CoQ is important in metabolism and considered good nutrition by some, though hard scientific proof is not plentiful. The active ingredients in popular plants of a health food nature, such as gingko or ginseng, would be considered nutraceuticals. A better understanding of this class of nutrients can be gained by considering a particular one, omega-3 fatty acids.

There is reference to omega fatty acids in human nutrition literature from 20 years ago, and awareness, but not clear understanding, has slowly spread to most human nutrition technicians. As a background for this discussion, a review of basic biochemistry and then human data would be helpful.

Although technically acids, fatty acids are a bit misleading as a term in that the basic concept is better served if we use the simple term "fat" instead of fatty acid. Fat molecules are one of nature's ways of storing energy and this is done by building long strings of carbon atoms. Structurally, fats are different from carbohydrates that are rings of carbon atoms and differ from proteins that are carbon and nitrogen in strings and branches. A brief review of fats covered in Chapter 2: Common fat molecules are up to 22 carbons in a row, with varying amounts of hydrogen attached. If there is a lot of hydrogen, it is called a saturated fat, meaning it cannot hold any more hydrogen; it is saturated with hydrogen. If some hydrogen is missing, it is an unsaturated fat, and if a lot of hydrogen is missing, it is called a polyunsaturated fat, usually abbreviated PUFA. Saturated fat tends to be solid and come from animals (tallow, lard), while unsaturated fat tends to come from plants and be in oil form (corn oil, palm oil). These are all terms you've heard for years, along with allegations of what is healthy and good and what is unhealthy and bad.

Omega-3 means three carbon molecules from the end of the carbon chain there is hydrogen missing. Omega-6 means six carbons from the end there is hydrogen missing. It is intriguing the difference three carbons can have on the effect of a missing hydrogen molecule. In the modern North American diet, there is a lot of omega-6 fatty acid. Omega-6s are not bad in and of themselves, except their high level tends to exclude omega-3s. Because it is not a matter of one must be as high as possible and the other as low as possible, human nutritionists talk in terms of the ratio of omega-3 to omega-6.

There is close relationship between the omega-3 content of a person's diet and protection from heart attack. High omega-6 along with low omega-3 diet intake greatly increases the incidence of heart attack in a population. This is established fact for humans. But dogs and cats are not susceptible to hardening of the arteries or heart disease so the worry of excess omega-6 in their diet is unwarranted. However, it is known that omega-3s do several other good things (in proper ratio with omega-6s) for people and pets.

Fish oil is the highest known natural source of omega-3 fatty acids. Fish oil is good. It is also very unstable, going rancid at the slightest excuse, so don't try to supplement your own fish oil. One day on the garage shelf during a hot summer and your fish oil will be useless and your money wasted. Additionally, not all fish oils are equal. Cold water fish (salmon, trout) are better than warm water fish (catfish, tilapia). Sex of the fish and season of the year can have large influence on omega-3 content of the oil, and some species, sadly, are loaded with PCBs and mercury.

The active omega-3 fatty acids in fish oil, EPA and DHA (eicosapentaenoic acid and docosapentaenoic acid) have 20 and 22 carbons, and it requires a sophisticated lab to quantify them. You do not want to feed just any fish oil to your pet. It is important to buy from a supplier who understands distillation of these products, because that is how they are purified of harmful contaminants, and their poor stability requires accurate mixing with antioxidants. Encapsulated pills from health food stores are a good source.

Omega-3 fatty acids are beneficial in very small amounts and promote the synthesis of hormone-like substances. For example, apparently in cows, fish oil can help with maternal recognition of early pregnancy lessening the incidence of early embryonic mortality. You may well be saying to yourself, "Cows don't eat fish. Why would nature have them benefit from some fish ingredient?" In truth, fish oil is actually supplying fatty acids that the cow can make for itself under proper conditions and given adequate precursors. Fish oil is just an efficient way to jump to the end of the process.

But most feed ingredients are not good sources of omega-3 fatty acids. Indeed, corn oil and soybean oil are better sources of omega-6 fatty acids. Pets, like people, usually are not lacking omega-6s. However, like people, pets are often in a position to benefit from omega-3 supplementation.

Concerning horses, not all grasses are good sources, and even those that do contain omega-3s suffer greatly from oxidation when dried in the sun and stored for months. Considering the insight about early pregnancy recognition in cows, there probably is a good argument for supplementing brood mares with omega-3s, especially given the absurd custom of all race horses being a year older on January 1st.

MICRONUTRIENT DIFFERENCES FOR DOGS AND CATS

Most readily appreciate that cats need more protein than dogs. Assuming equal protein quality, dogs require 20 percent in their diet while cats require 30 percent. Concerning vitamins and trace minerals, dogs and cats have far more in common than not, but the differences are worthy of note. The plant pigment β-carotene (the yellow and orange color of many fruits and vegetables) serves as a vitamin A precursor for many animals. Dogs have the metabolic capability to cleave a molecule of β-carotene into an active molecule of vitamin A. Cats lack this capability so must have all their vitamin A provided by their diet. Nutrient recommendation tables (see Table 13, Appendix) show cats as needing nearly twice the vitamin A of dogs.

Fat metabolism in cats has one specific difference from dogs. Cats possess very low levels of the enzyme delta-six-desaturase (Δ6-desaturase) needed for the process of elongating fatty acids. Because the dog has this enzyme, it requires only the precursor, linoleic acid, which is metabolized on to arachidonic acid. Experts in this field recommend that arachidonic acid be included in cat diets but not the diet of the dog.

Dogs can use sulfur amino acids to make taurine but carnivores lack this capability. Thus, cats have a requirement for the amino acid taurine, as it is possible to cause a deficiency (one symptom is blindness) on a diet too low in taurine. Taurine, a free amino acid and not used in proteins, is abundant in animal tissue so a cat diet including animal tissue will provide plentiful taurine. A cat diet deriving its protein from vegetable sources requires taurine supplementation. Once again we see the eloquence of the mutation-survival advantage system of evolution. Taurine is plentiful in carnivore prey species, obviating the need for its synthesis by carnivores. Herbivores and omnivores on the other hand, do not encounter taurine in their diet, so retain the capability to synthesize it. This amino acid is readily available to pet food manufacturers commercially.

The cat lacks the ability to make niacin from the dietary precursor tryptophan, whereas the dog is able to meet its needs, at least partially, from this amino acid. However, cats consuming animal tissue, which is high in NAD and NADP (nicotinamide adenine dinucleotide phosphate), as would be the case in the wild, do not need niacin.

The B vitamin biotin is required by both the dog and the cat, and the authors of the NRC allow that feed ingredients and intestinal microflora production answer this need for both species. These authorities recommend including biotin for the cat, but not the dog. There is a compound in raw egg white called avadin that very efficiently binds and inactivates biotin, so continued use of raw egg in a diet will soon lead to a biotin deficiency for a dog or cat.

From the foregoing, one can deduce that, according to the American Association of Feed Control Officials (AAFCO), dog food is a dubious diet for cats, and the marketplace offers few diets advertised as proper for both dogs and cats. What about the other alternative, cat food fed to dogs? Ignoring the extra expense, cat food fed to dogs would provide more protein and vitamins than required (with one exception) but none beyond the safe upper limit. The one exception among the vitamins would be pantothenate, recommended for the dog at 12mg/kg of diet, and 5mg/kg for the cat. Macro and micro mineral recommendations for the two species do differ (compare Table 13 and Table 14 in the Appendix) but other than zinc a cat diet would suffice for a dog. The AAFCO recommendation for dogs of 120 ppm zinc is three to four times most all other species, and also differs from the NRC levels. The NRC authorities recommend a level of 60 ppm for adult maintenance, but allow that the minimum requirement for puppies is 40 ppm. The 75 ppm zinc of a cat diet is sufficient for the dog, in my opinion.

REFERENCES

Taubes, G. 2007. *Good Calories, Bad Calories. Challenging Conventional Wisdom on Diet, Weight Control and Disease.* Alfred A. Knopf. New York. pg 321.

high soluble carbohydrate diets increase the need for vitamins... Carpenter, KJ. 2000. *Beriberi, White Rice, and Vitamin B: A Disease, a Cause and a Cure.* University of California press. Berkeley., CA. pg 213-218.

those suffering metabolic syndrome have lower Vitamin C... Ford, ES, AH Mokdad, WH Giles, DW Brown. 2003. *The metabolic syndrome and antioxidant concentrations: Findings of the Third National Health and Nutrition Examination Survey.* Diabetes. 52 (9): 2346-2352.

compete for the same transfer site... Will, JC, and T. Byers. 1996. *Does Diabetes Mellitus increase the requirement for Vitamin C?* Nutrition Reviews 54:193-202.

infusing glucose causes blood Vitamin C to drop... Cox, BD, MJ Whichelow, JW Butterfield, P Nichols. 1974. *Peripheral vitamin C metabolism in diabetics and non-diabetics: Effect of intra-arterial insulin.* Clinical Science and Molecular Medicine. 47 (I):63-72.

assembled a provocative set of data... Liu, S. 2005. *Dietary carbohydrates, whole grains, and the risk of Type 2 Diabetes Mellitus. in Whole-grain foods in health and disease.* L. Marquart, JL Slavin, R. Gary, eds. Amer. Assoc. of Cereal Chemists. 3340 Pilot Knob, St. Paul, MN. 55121. pg 168.

humans possess all the DNA to make Vitamin C... Lucock, M. 2007. *Molecular Nutrition and Genomics. Nutrition and the Ascent of Humankind.* John Wiley and Sons, Inc. Hoboken, NJ.

cats and probably dogs gain no advantage from sunshine... Morris, J. 1999. *Ineffective vitamin D synthesis in cats is reversed by an inhibitor of 7-dehyrdocholesterol-Δ7–reductase.* J. Nutr. 129:903-909.

fish oil can help with maternal recognition of early pregnancy... Burke, JM, CR Staples, CA Risco, RL De La Sota, WW Thatcher. 1997. *Effect of ruminant grade menhaden fish meal on reproductive performance of lactating dairy cows.* J. Dairy Sci. 80:3386-3398.

dogs can use sulfur containing amino acids to make taurine... Delaney, SJ., PH Kass, QR Rogers, AJ Fascetti. 2003. *Plasma and whole blood taurine in normal dogs of varying size fed commercially prepared food.* J. Am. Physiol. Ani. Nutr. 87:236-244.

Carnivores lack this ability (to make taurine)... Chesney, RW. 1985. *Taurine: Its biological role and clinical implications.* Adv. Pediatr. 32:1-42.

the cat lacks the ability to make niacin... Leklem, JE., RR Brown, LV Hankes, M Schmaeler. 1971. *Tryptophan metabolism in the cat: A study with carbon-14 labeled compounds.* Am.J. Vet. Res. 32:335-344.

cats possess very low levels of delta-six desaturase... Pawlowsky, RA, A Barnes, N. Nelson. 1994. Essential fatty acid metabolism in the feline; Relationship between liver and brain production of long chain polyunsaturated fatty acids. J. Lipid Res. 35:2032-2040... and, Rivers, JP, AJ Sinclair, MA Crawford. 1975. Inability of the cat to desaturate essential fatty acids. Nature 258:171-173.

120 ppm zinc for dog four times other species... AAFCO. 2009. Official Publication, American Association of Feed Control Officials. Oxford, IN, 47971. http://www.aafco.org... and, NRC. 2006. Nutrient Requirements of Dogs and Cats. National Research Council. National Academies Press, 500 Fifth Street, N.W., Washington, DC, 20001.

11

MINERALS

You'll find this chapter easier to read than some others because the roadway has less curves and the white lines are more evident.

Minerals are small distinct nutrients with relatively less complicated roles in metabolism. Minerals are generally divided into two categories, macro and micro. The macro minerals are calcium, phosphorus, sodium, potassium, magnesium, sulfur and chlorine. Each is found in the diet at about 0.5 to one percent of the dry matter. The micro (trace) minerals, found at levels considerably below one percent, are usually listed in the diet as parts per million, which is the same as a milligram per kilogram.

Minerals are not often found in nature as simple, unattached elements. Each is attached to some other mineral. For example, if calcium is needed in a formula in addition to that provided by the natural ingredients, it is added as calcium carbonate, which is 40 percent calcium. Phosphorus is sometimes increased in a food by the addition of monocalcium-dicalcium phosphate, which is 18 to 21 percent phosphorus. Thus, the total sum of all the minerals in a food, called ash, is always greater than the sum of the simple elements of nutritional interest. Called ash because it is the residue of a food burned at a very high temperature, its content in a good quality pet food on a dry matter basis is eight to 10 percent or less.

Unattached minerals are very unhappy and often harmful. Sodium and chlorine, in combination, make salt, which we eat every day. Sodium in pure form is so reactive it must be stored in petroleum oil. A small piece of sodium placed on water bursts into flame, and a larger chunk will explode. Pure chlorine is a colorless, odorless gas, tasteless and quickly lethal if inhaled. But sodium and chlorine find each other in nature, combining and canceling their reactivity. In dilute concentrations, such as the salt in sea water, sodium and chloride can divorce from each other and exist in free, unattached form, which is what happens in our blood and cells.

But free mineral elements are always on the hunt to attach, or switch to something of stronger attachment, and this reactivity is often the reason for their role in biology, usually as cofactors in enzymatic reactions. Pure elements are always found combined with something else, in a lowered state of reactivity. Copper, for example, as used in a pet food, is always attached to a carbonate molecule or a sulfate or an oxygen. This is the case for all the mineral supplements.

Minerals are usually not as well adsorbed as other nutrients in the diet. Where protein and fat will be from 80 to 95 percent taken into the intestinal cell, individual mineral elements tend to be absorbed at about 30 to 50 percent, but there are exceptions such as sodium at 99 percent. Some mineral sources, infamously oxides such as iron oxide, are very poorly absorbed. Iron oxide is the same thing as rust, and is about one to four percent digested. It does make a red (rust) color, and is often used in mineral mixes to impart color. Its iron contribution is nearly useless nutritionally.

As a generalization, a mineral in the sulfate form is better digested than the carbonate form, which is better than the oxide form. A fourth form, the chloride, is not often a consideration. While of good bioavailability, it is expensive, and the inclusion of inexpensive salt, sodium chloride, tends to add the needed chlorine. The cost of the three common forms also tends to follow the same hierarchy; sulfates cost more than carbonates, which cost more than oxides. *For more on mineral, see End Notes page 168.*

Historically, suppliers of minerals and mineral premixes have added one percent oil to control the dustiness of their products. The oil used actually came to be called mineral oil, its use for this purpose was so commonplace. Mineral oil, also known as petrolatum, is liquid and certainly oily and does a good job of minimizing dust in minerals, but it is actually a petroleum based product. It is often used as a base in ointments, but it is of no nutritional value. Even though it delivers no nutrition, it can be absorbed and over a lifetime can build up in an animal.

I have met with little success in dissuading mineral suppliers from using this product because the alternatives have major drawbacks. Other oils, such as corn oil, are just as effective, but cost much more and eventually go rancid. Further, no paying customer has ever complained to them about their use of mineral oil. And that ends the story on that topic. Nothing is going to change here until some mainstream newspaper carries an investigative report of a lawsuit where a pathologist expert witness showed slides of tissues full of petrolatum blobs from a dead endangered species.

Candidly, it may not be a problem. In its two year life span, a feedlot steer might consume one pound of petrolatum and absorb 13 grams of it. There probably are more critical things to concern oneself about.

But what of the elephant in a zoo, fed grain containing minerals with this oil, every day for 50 years? A fundamental problem of our agricultural based animal feed system is that in agriculture, nothing lives long enough to die. Chickens are golden nuggets at eight or even six weeks of age. Beef is in the grocery store meat case at

24 months of age. Pork chops come from swine that are less than a year old. The point here is not to criticize our food production system. The point is that our pets, horses and zoo animals live long full lives; the longer the better.

The basis of nearly all our insight about animal nutrition has historically come from production agriculture, where the emphasis has been on anything but longevity. In fact, it has been exactly the opposite; get animals to slaughter size as fast as possible, end their lives as soon as we can. To correct this, and there are many who are trying, will require patience. To determine what exact diet favors a longer life in just about any companion animal would require an experiment running for at least a dozen years.

MACRO MINERALS

Calcium: The mineral element found in the body in the highest concentration is calcium. In an 80 lb dog, about 420 grams (.92 lb) would be calcium, and 99 percent is in the bone. Proportionally, cats have slightly more calcium. Bone calcium is combined with phosphorus in a compound called hydroxyapatite. The greatest dietary need is when bones and teeth are being formed. Calcium plays an important role in other aspects of physiology, such as muscle contraction, blood clotting and nerve impulses. Life without these functions would be short indeed.

In the blood, there are two principle forms of calcium, bound and free. Physiologists also call these two different forms pools or compartments. The free form is readily available to apply to calcium type work, while the bound form serves as a reserve to replenish the free form. Blood calcium levels are carefully protected. This means that there can be a calcium lack in the diet and blood readings will indicate there is no problem. This is because bone reserves are mobilized to sustain blood levels. Said another way, when blood calcium levels are low, there is a big problem. Proper blood levels are essential for moment to moment life of body cells, and are one of the last things allowed to falter in a deficiency. Bone will be dissolved for weeks or even months and its calcium put into circulation to keep blood levels adequate.

One of the best illustrations of calcium metabolism is a problem of hypocalcemia (low blood calcium) in new mothers, sometimes referred to as milk fever. As the mammary glands quickly increase in production of milk, the demand for calcium can sometimes outpace the immediate supply of the two blood pools. In a day or two, hormonal adjustments will bring bone calcium into play, but in the meantime, if the diet is deficient in digestible calcium, a critical blood shortage of calcium causes serious problems, with several systems involved. Milk production is automatically reduced in an effort to restore balance, and if the case is not too severe, mobilized bone reserves soon right the ship. Intervention with IV calcium can be one of the most striking repairs in medicine. Mothers that can barely raise their head will jump up even before treatment is complete and return to their litter. That is calcium. It's important.

But a calcium deficiency is rare in dogs fed commercial diets. Milk and dairy products are great sources, as is alfalfa, usually about 1.5 to 2.0 percent, but these are not common pet food ingredients. Some horses are fed alfalfa, while many horse owners avoid alfalfa, saying it makes their horse "hot" (discussed in Chapter 8 specific to horse nutrition). Pet foods sometimes include meat and bone meal, or bone meal. These are high in calcium. To whatever extend the diet falls short of calcium supplied by the ingredients, the difference is usually made up using an inorganic source, like monocalcium-dicalcium or calcium carbonate (limestone). Natural formulations will often include bone meal, which is about 30 percent calcium, and has the advantage that this calcium is in the hydroxyapatite linkage with phosphorus, just as an omnivore would derive from the animal portion of its diet.

There is a calcium deficiency once common in dogs fed exclusively raw meat, and rarely seen nowadays. Meat alone, without the bones and cartilage attached, and especially organ meats, is quite low in phosphorus averaging 0.17 percent, and the calcium is woefully low, almost to the point of completely absent. Organ meats run 0.01 percent calcium. The recommended levels of calcium and phosphorus in puppy diets is 1.2 and 1.0 percent, respectively.

Growing dogs fed only meat soon develop what is called nutritional secondary hypoparathyroidism, meaning low blood calcium and phosphorus caused by diet. The bones are thin and weak, usually bending under the weight of the growing dog, and puppies will break their bones simply trying to play. Early in my career, my colleagues ran feeding trials that exposed this failing in some commercial dog foods. Publishing the trial results was all it took to end the practice of selling pet food unbalanced for macro minerals. In these trials, after the pathology became evident, the pups were fed a proper diet and went on to attain normal adult size and bone structure.

I don't think the bad diets were a deliberate aim of the pet food company. I would like to think it was ignorance, as the cure, adding a little calcium and phosphorus to the formula, cost them nearly nothing.

There would appear to be a fairly high tolerance for dietary calcium, with one important warning. Calcium must always be more than phosphorus. If phosphorus is higher than calcium, it tends to bind the calcium and other minerals, and reduce bioavailability. I will return to this topic later when I discuss chelated minerals, which can overcome the inhibitions by other minerals and anti-metabolites. While phosphorus is recommended for a growing pet in a range of 1.0 percent of the dry matter, calcium can run as high as 2.5 percent or even a little more, without undue harm.

Phosphorus: The body pool of phosphorus is maintained by intestinal uptake and renal excretion. As with all such balancing acts of the body, there are numerous signals, checks and feedbacks by hormones, receptor sites and messenger molecules.

Phosphorus, like calcium, is found predominantly in the bone. Eighty-five percent of the total body phosphorus is in the bone, about 14 percent in the soft tissues, and one percent in the extracellular compartment. Besides its role in the skeleton, phosphorus is indispensable as a component of DNA, RNA, cell membranes (as phospholipids) and ATP, a molecule that is the energetic spark plug for all of life. Needless to say, life as we know it would be impossible without phosphorus, and just as for calcium, blood levels are maintained even at high cost. A diet for growth that is one percent phosphorus on a dry matter basis is quite adequate, with 0.5 percent sufficient for most other life stages.

Foods used for animals tend to have good levels of phosphorus. Plant seeds are a reliable source so this means soybean meal, corn, milo, wheat, etc., are dependable sources of phosphorus.

However, in cereals and vegetables, a significant amount of the phosphorus can be in the form of phytate (inositol with six phosphorus molecules attached), which is poorly digested. Phytate can be a problem for other minerals as well, making them indigestible. This has led to the introduction in the market of commercial phytase, an enzyme that breaks the inositol hold on phosphorus. The yeasts used in leavening breads produce a phytase, so the phosphorus of bread grains are more available. Other pet food ingredients that are good sources of phosphorus are meat, bone meal and fish meal. Practically speaking, a phosphorus deficiency is not encountered very often in animals, wild or domestic.

Magnesium: Magnesium is required in the diet at around 0.3 percent of the dry matter (0.4 percent for growth in puppies), and most of it is supplied by the feed ingredients. Deficiencies are rare, except as secondary to other disease. When feed ingredients fall short of needs, the usual supplement turned to is magnesium oxide, which runs about 58 percent, and is fairly well absorbed. Another source sometimes used is magnesium sulfate, which is about 17 percent magnesium.

Magnesium is required in literally hundreds of different metabolic reactions and tissues. Half of all body magnesium is found in the bone but unlike calcium, it is not accessible as backup to repair low blood levels. Its homeostatic controls are the same as for other minerals, intestinal uptake balanced by renal excretion. An affliction of herbivores encountered more frequently in the spring of the year is called grass tetany, caused by low blood magnesium. Characterized by rigid muscles, the medical profession calls it hypomagnesaemia. Rapidly growing new plants at the beginning of the warm season of lengthening daylight can sometimes have lowered magnesium levels, so herbivores eating exclusively these fresh forages can be prone to grass tetany.

Sodium: Sodium is another mineral essential for life. Salt is one ingredient that dogs show a preference for in taste tests. Being so inexpensive, it tends to be included in pet foods at higher levels than needed nutritionally. There is only a small reserve of sodium in the body, with balance regulated by uptake from the intestine countered by excretion from the kidneys. About 40 percent of the body's salt is in the bone, half of which is considered accessible. The remaining 60 percent is in cells and interstitial fluid. Virtually all sodium consumed crosses the gut wall into the body, and feces are nearly devoid of sodium.

In species that don't sweat, the kidney is by far the major excretion route. A deficiency of either component of salt – sodium or chlorine – can drive a craving in animals. When lacking salt, a person or animal will show a noticeable increase in their appetite for salt or salty foods. I am not aware of any other mineral deficiency causing such a specific taste preference.

A lack of other minerals, if severe enough, will lead to a behavior called pica: an urge to eat many strange things, especially dirt. (Note: The common behavior of dogs eating horse or cow manure, and frequently cat feces, is not pica. It is not abnormal or indicative of any known dietary imbalance, and aside from our esthetic concern, causes no harm. It may be driven by an instinctual need to augment an imbalanced gut microflora. All feces are high in bacteria.) The principle role of sodium, in conjunction with chloride and potassium, is fluid balance, or osmoregulation. The sodium content of serum, as well as of other minerals, mirrors that of sea water, where all life began. As life forms evolved out of the sea, an efficient means of regulating the internal fluid mineral balance was crucial. This chore is managed very precisely by the kidney.

Some years ago, I was involved in research where we tried to establish a sodium deficiency in German Shepherds. Removing salt from the diet did nothing. Providing only distilled, deionized drinking water did nothing. Not until purified feed ingredients were added to the protocol, selected for the total absence of sodium, did sodium deficiency begin to appear. Even then, it required some months. Sodium is so critical to life that the kidney can virtually shut down its elimination.

Chloride: Most nutrition books only discuss chloride in conjunction with sodium, as intake of salt, the predominant source of sodium, which invariably brings along a proper balance of chloride. Both these molecules, along with potassium, work hand in glove to orchestrate fluid balance throughout the body. It is possible to induce a deficiency specific for chloride, but it is most uncommon in pets. In high producing dairy cows, it is common to feed sodium bicarbonate to buffer the rumen, and unless salt is reduced in the diet, sodium can become too elevated in the diet. However, with too much salt reduction, chloride can become deficient. Most chloride is in the extracellular fluids, with most of the remainder in collagen, where it is also readily accessible.

Sulfur: Sulfur is an exception to the foregoing discussion about mineral combinations and bonds with other elements. Though often attached to other minerals, such as the sulfate in magnesium sulfate, sulfur will also exist happily with only other sulfur molecules. Nutrition texts are surprisingly silent in most instances on the topic of sulfur. Sulfur is widespread in feeds and foods, especially those high in quality protein, averaging 0.1 percent across all feedstuffs, and comprising a unique and critical part of the essential amino acids methionine and cystein. Selenium and sulfur are quite similar in molecular structure, providing an avenue for yeast to incorporate selenium into the place normally reserved for sulfur in methionine; this allows the marketing of a source of organic selenium. However improved in bioavailability this selenium replacing sulfur may be, the chemical bonds in such supplements are not the traditional chelate form.

Potassium: The average of all feeds for potassium is 1.0 percent, quite high as minerals go. Potassium is found in pet foods at adequate levels almost by accident, and due to its widespread nature, it is nearly impossible to formulate a potassium deficient diet using conventional foods. Potassium is over 1.5 percent of an animal's weight, and found almost exclusively within the cells where it is all readily available for use. Regulated by the kidney, one of its main functions as the primary cat ion (positive charge) is membrane polarization, essential for muscle contraction, particularly in the heart.

TRACE MINERALS

Required in the diet in microscopic amounts, trace minerals are essential in nutrition as seen by the many problems encountered when they are deficient. Their role is often as cofactors of enzymes that run every aspect of metabolism. Minerals in this class of nutrients are copper, cobalt, iron, manganese, zinc, iodine, selenium and chromium. Others such as boron and arsenic are suspected to be important but the levels are not determined. Trace minerals are used in supplements most often bonded to sulfate, carbonate or oxygen. Trace minerals in the diet can sometimes be found in another type of attachment called chelates, discussed in more detail below.

Iron: Iron oxide (rust) is known to be only three or four percent digestible. Thus, animal diets usually employ iron sulfate or iron carbonate to fortify diets. Trace amounts of iron are spread throughout the array of pet food ingredients as an endogenous nutrient in the food, and also because iron is encountered frequently in food and feed handling equipment. In some minerals used to augment dietary levels of macro minerals, such as calcium carbonate (limestone) or dicalcium phosphate, iron can be 1,000 ppm (parts per million) or more. Hemoglobin of the red blood cell is the site of 67 percent of the body's iron, with macrophages (immune defense) accounting for 27 percent, and myoglobin of muscle contains four percent. Besides its role in oxygen transport in the blood and muscle, iron is part of the cytochrome enzyme system found in all forms of life and essential to energy metabolism. Inadequate iron intake eventually presents as anemia.

Copper: The bodies of dogs and cats contain only small amounts of copper but it is essential. Liver is the principle location, where copper is bound to metallothionein. From there, it is repackaged for circulation. Copper has many functions physiologically, including the cytochrome C system (energy metabolism), as a cofactor for the enzyme superoxide dismutase (protection from oxidative damage) and in the metabolism of iron. It is possible that an iron deficiency anemia symptom can actually be caused by a copper deficiency. Zinc is an effective anti-metabolite for copper, as is molybdenum. In a diet that assays as adequate for copper, there can be a de facto copper deficiency if molybdenum or zinc is too high.

A hereditary defect in Bedlington Terriers can lead to toxic accumulation of copper. The anti-metabolite function of zinc and molybdenum can actually be used to therapeutically treat these terriers. Because of its role in pigment formation, copper deficiency can cause black coated animals to have red hairs.

Cobalt: Current insight about cobalt feeding to dogs and cats is that there is no point, which explains why it is not listed in the NRC tables of requirements. The rationale is that intestinal microflora can incorporate cobalt into the vitamin cobalamine, and even though this occurs after the site of absorption, adequate absorption occurs. Cobalt's main functions, through its role as a component of B12, is involved in red blood cell production. Because monogastric diets include this vitamin in animal ingredients of the feed, its deficiency is quite infrequent. Most all pet foods are supplemented with B12.

Manganese: Distributed throughout the body of the dog (12 mg) and cat (2 mg), levels are quite low, with the liver and kidney somewhat higher. A cofactor or activator in enzyme systems, it is known to be essential for normal bone growth, cartilage formation and nerve function. Zinc and manganese compete for the same binding sites, so excess of one can induce a deficiency of the other.

Zinc: The most abundant mineral element inside the cell, zinc is involved in over 200 enzymes and is critical for membrane integrity and essential for immunity. It is known in some species that an offspring born to a dam deficient in zinc has a compromised immune capability at birth, and no amount of zinc supplementation at any point later in life will restore full immune capability. There is a growing school of thought that there is more than one maintenance requirement. It is suspected the level of intake adequate in health becomes inadequate during an immune challenge. Zinc is well identified as playing a role in wound healing, and known to be integral to integument health (skin, hair, horn, hoof).

Iodine: Thyroid hormone and its biologically active form require iodine. These hormones control the rate of metabolism in adults and growth in the young. No other role for this element is known. Feeds of inland animal origin are poor sources of iodine, while those derived from the sea or near the sea are richer iodine sources. Salt condensed from sea water is a rich source.

Selenium: Of all the minerals, selenium is one of the few (along with chromium) to actually endure a measure of government regulation, with specific levels of toxicity, and maximum levels of allowable supplementation, declared for agriculture animals. This trace mineral is needed in the diet on the order of two to three tenths of a part per million, or 200 to 300 parts per billion (ppb). For comparison, a part per billion is one minute since Christ was born. Selenium is frequently found in forages and grains but there are a few areas of the world where it is known to be deficient in the soil.

In a bygone era, when animals spent their entire life in a small geography, and feeds were all procured in the same small region, it was possible to encounter a selenium deficiency in livestock if it was a selenium deficient area. A selenium deficiency today is unlikely for several reasons. Grains are marketed all over the globe, from coast to coast and continent to continent. The probability is very low that an animal has been fed the same food from the same selenium deficient region for the past year or more. Additionally, virtually every manufactured grain, vitamin and mineral supplement has selenium included in the formula.

It is frequently noted that selenium and vitamin E are antioxidants, and it is true that each is involved in cellular metabolism of free radicals, but they operate in separate compartments of the cell, with different roles, and can only partially spare each other. Each has a specific requirement in the diet. The presence of one does not permit the absence of the other.

It is recommended that animals consume a diet that is about 0.3 mg of selenium per kilogram of dry diet. A mature horse, for example, will eat about 25 to 30 lb of totally dry feed each day, and 2.5 mg of elemental selenium will be a very adequate supplement. A pound of elemental selenium will provide 2.5 mg for 500 years, so it should be obvious that supplementation of selenium is best left to professional feed manufacturers. Due to the very low level of inclusion in a diet, selenium is usually marketed to mineral premix blenders as the sodium salt form (sodium selenite) in a dilute concentration of one to four percent. A pet food company buys these pre-assembled mineral mixes and adds them to formulas in controlled portions.

Selenium cannot form a chelate. Chelate means an exact and specific molecular bonding, and selenium is not physically capable of forming such a bond without violating the laws of the universe. But organic selenium, derived from yeast cultures that accumulate high levels, offers a more bioavailable source.

CHELATES

Nature has high regard for chelates, using them in leading roles. The iron in hemoglobin is in a chelate form, as is the magnesium in chlorophyll. These two molecules, hemoglobin used for oxygen transport in animals, and chlorophyll required for photosynthesis in plants, can be argued as molecules of import second to none in all of biology.

Some years ago when radioactive compounds were less regulated, researchers in the US grew corn on soil containing radioactive Zn^{65} and used the resulting silage crop as an ingredient in a diet for calves. Due to the radiotracer, zinc concentration in this silage was known, and a second feed of identical zinc content from zinc chloride was formulated as a control ingredient. Upon analysis, it was reported that calves fed the radiolabeled corn silage showed 40 percent more zinc in their metabolically active tissue than those fed the same dose as a mineral supplement. The explanation of why zinc from a plant shows higher bioavailability than from a mineral supplement is not known to this day. Regardless, this classic work demonstrated that nature's understanding of trace minerals is superior to our custom of supplementing organic dusts and powders. Could the difference be chelates?

A chelated mineral is one that has formed a specific type of chemical bond (coordinate-covalent) with one or more other molecules, usually protein. Several companies manufacture chelated minerals serving as the source of supply for the animal feed and human health food industries. Chelated minerals, also referred to loosely as organic minerals, are eight to 15 percent purity, depending on manufacturer, and are more expensive than inorganic minerals but they have important advantages.

Divalent metals like copper, manganese and zinc form the strongest chelates. It is theorized chelates can overcome inhibition by protecting a mineral from binding with other minerals or phytate that are in excess. A diet high in one mineral, frequently iron, can depress the bioavailability of other minerals, presumably by competitively excluding the other minerals from binding sites. Another example is high molybdenum binding copper, or inhibiting its absorption. This can be a problem in hay, where molybdenum can sometimes be 10 or more parts per million (ppm). This molybdenum combines with copper, and an otherwise adequate diet produces copper deficiency. When assayed for copper, the feed will yield laboratory results that indicate an adequate amount for proper health, but in fact, the copper in the diet is not available to the animal. This problem is easily overcome by the addition of only five ppm of copper in the chelated form. The reason is that the chelated copper can overcome or avoid the inhibition caused by the molybdenum.

The exact way this happens is not known, but it almost certainly involves protection of the copper molecule by its protein carrier (called a ligand) before it is presented to the gut wall for absorption. This is an active field of research, with many scientific papers demonstrating advantages of chelated mineral supplements. The precise mechanism of action of chelates remains a mystery at this time, despite what some sales literature might boast. It is suspected that the route of absorption for chelates differs from inorganic minerals.

For example, it has been demonstrated that a chelated mineral, once absorbed into the body, is retained better than if it originated as an inorganic mineral. Many trials investigating zinc chelates also include chelated copper and manganese in the same treatment, making it impossible to determine which mineral was responsible for the result. Nonetheless, there is ample evidence to support the efficacy of chelated minerals. One just has to be circumspect about accepting all conclusions pushed by ambitious sales programs. Researchers in the lab of Clarence Ammerman at the University of Florida have shown that chelated minerals from different manufacturers can vary a fair amount in bioavailability.

REFERENCES

deficient in zinc has compromised immune capability... Beach, RS., ME Gershwin, LS Hurley. 1982. Gestational zinc deprivation in mice: Persistence of immunodeficiency for three generations. Science. 218:469.

40 percent more zinc in their metabolically active tissue... Neathery, MW, S. Rachmat, WJ Miller, RP Gentry, DM Blackburn. 1972. Effect of chemical form on orally administered 65zinc on absorption and metabolism in cattle. Proc. Soc. Exp. Biol. 139:953-956.

chelated mineral, once absorbed is retained better... Lardy, GP, MS Kerley, JA Paterson. 1992. Retention of chelated metal proteinates by lambs. J. Anim. Sci. 70 (suppl. 1) 314 (Abstr.)...and, Nockels, CE, J. DeBonis, J. Torrent. 1993. Stress induction affects copper and zinc balance in calves fed organic and inorganic copper and zinc sources. J. Anim. Sci. 71:2539-2545...and, Spears, JW. 1989. Zinc methionine in ruminants: Relative bioavailability of zinc in lambs and effect of growth and performance of growing heifers. J. Anim. Sci. 67: 835-843.

chelated minerals from different manufacturers can vary in bioavailability ... Cao, J, PR Henry, R Guo, RA Howerda, JP Roth, RC Littell, RD Miles, CB Ammerman. 2000. Chemical characteristics and relative bioavailability of supplemental organic zinc sources for poultry and ruminants. J. Anim. Sci. 78:2039-2054.

12

PET FOOD REGULATIONS

When buying pet food, you have to rely on the label of the product to provide information for your decision making process. It is not the ambition here to cover this topic in detail, as it is tangential to animal nutrition, but some discussion is required as whatever food you might buy for your animal, even hay, is covered by regulations about its nutrients. Of course there is price and price per unit of weight, but all appreciate this is not necessarily indicative of the best value. All pet food products must declare on the label what animal the product is for. To inform even illiterate customers, products always display a picture of either a dog or a cat.

Besides the net weight, manufacturer and address, there must also be declared a minimum guarantee and list of ingredients. The minimum guarantee is a statement of a few simple analysis numbers (protein, fat, fiber and moisture, in percent) that the manufacturer guarantees to be true. The list of ingredients shows what was used to make the product, printed in descending order of preponderance, meaning the most used ingredient in the formula is listed first and the least used is listed last. Most bag products list a feeding guide, based on the size of the pet and the caloric density of the food, and many bags list a typical analysis. Typical analysis is different from guaranteed analysis. Showing far more nutrients, it is an indication of what the manufacturer has targeted in formulating his product, and usually is useful insight. However, contrary to label claim guarantees, no inspection or sampling tests are performed for nutrients shown on the label as typical analysis.

Label information is provided as a protection for pet owners and their pets, and also for the protection of pet food industry members. Not just consumers, but also reputable companies are harmed by unscrupulous suppliers. Label information is further intended to enable consumers to make informed buying decisions by comparing different products.

This system is not without its limitations, but by and large, it works well and is far better than nothing. The industry is guided by the Association of American Feed Control Officials, referred to as AAFCO, which had its origin over 100 years ago as the agricultural feed industry began to commercialize. AAFCO has numerous committees (among them collaborative check sample, enforcement issues, inspection and sampling, contaminants, laboratory methods, labeling, ingredient definition) including a pet food committee. Each committee, made up of feed industry professionals, has up to a dozen expert advisors from industry and government.

One of the most active committees is ingredient definitions. If a feed is used in a pet food, it must be on the label, and to be on the label, it must have an official AAFCO definition. AAFCO serves as the reference authority for defining all feed descriptions in a uniform way. It is the standard that regulates and organizes commerce so that everyone agrees, for example, on the definition of hominy or mill run or meat and bone meal. The list of approved feeds is the longest single section of the regulations, at 93 pages out of 500. It is easy to grasp the commercial utility of an official distinction between what constitutes clean unadulterated corn and what is moldy corn, or corn of excess moisture.

A pet food company, selling millions of tons a year, is a huge opportunity for a supplier with an ingredient to sell, but a company lacking a definition for their product is essentially excluded from this market. The ingredient committee often finds itself as arbiter of substantial economic concerns for a company, as injudicious or hasty decisions by the committee can create an exclusive fortune for one company and make a pauper of its competitor. Impartiality and fairness are critical.

For a company to have its product listed as an ingredient with an approved definition can be a prolonged process. For example, metal proteinate (57.23), a type of organic mineral, was first proposed in 1967, adopted in 1970, amended in 1977 and again in 1987. At one point, there were over 25 different definitions for types of organic minerals. Indeed, mineral products are just one of 36 different feed ingredient categories, nearly 20 percent of the pages in this section.

AAFCO works closely with the Federal Drug Administration (FDA), the Center for Veterinary Medicine and the United States Department of Agriculture (USDA) and its division Animal Plant and Health Inspection Service (APHIS). All three of these agencies have a section dedicated specifically to working with the pet food industry. AAFCO has a memorandum of understanding with the FDA. AAFCO publishes a book every year of some 500 pages that provides guidance and governance for the industry. The organization's statement of purpose is to ensure nutrient content, efficacy and safety, develop standards and promote uniformity of laws, regulations and enforcement. They determine what is required, optional and prohibited on a label.

Enforcement of regulations is not done by AAFCO. This function is left to the individual state agriculture departments (or in a few instances, the state chemist's office). Over the years, AAFCO has painstakingly crafted what is called a Model

Bill, and the states are left to adopt it or not, as they wish. Most all do. The details spelled out by this Model Bill can be impressive. (Pet food company employees charged with complying with the Model Bill have been known to use different words to describe it.)

For example, the words "new" or "improved" must be substantiated and removed in six months. The word "proven" is forbidden unless substantiated by scientific evidence. If the name of a product includes an ingredient, such as "Hearty Meal with Lamb," lamb meat must be a minimum of three percent of the ingredient contents. Terms such as lean, low calorie, light, reduced fat, natural and tartar control are carefully proscribed and limited in permissible use. Even size of allowable type on the label is mandated. Without boring you with further details of the Model Bill (pet food regulations are 60 pages of the AAFCO manual) suffice it to say that the industry goes to great lengths to protect the pet.

There is one concept spelled out carefully in the regulations that pet owners need to understand. This is the matter referred to by industry professionals as nutritional adequacy, sometimes referred to as nutritionally complete. Four categories of nutrient density of pet food types are recognized in the regulations: gestation/lactation, growth, maintenance and all life stages. Unless the label clearly declares a product as a snack or treat, every product must state which of these four categories it qualifies for. The regulations contain tables listing exact requirements of the dog and the cat, for each life stage, for more than 30 nutrients.

Academicians and professional nutritionists use as their authority and reference a publication from the National Research Council (NRC) of the federal government. About once a decade this body gathers a committee of respected authorities on nutrition of a specific species and charges them with writing the latest knowledge into a succinct reference. The publication includes extensive text, with exceptions and qualifying conditions and the reader is always cautioned not to rely exclusively on the tables. These publications are available to the public, and it is actually the NRC recommendations that inform the AAFCO nutritional guidelines.

Upon request, a pet food manufacturer must submit a signed affidavit that their product meets the requirements for the species and life stage claimed. If a product fails to meet the requirements as shown by laboratory analysis, it can still qualify by actual scientific feeding trials. These trials, explained in exacting detail by AAFCO, are quite expensive, and few undertake to perform them.

However, it is important to note that by allowing this alternative method of proof of efficacy, AAFCO is recognizing that all their rules and declarations about adequacy and nutritional requirements may not be the last word, or fully enlightened.

It is allowed that if a product (tested according to their feeding protocol) enables a pet to have a full and healthy life, it does not matter to AAFCO what its nutrient profile is. However, a manufacturer must have the scientific feeding test results to prove a product's adequacy by this method, and its label may not reference the AAFCO nutrient profiles. They can claim on the label nutritional adequacy for the life stage tested.

REGULATIONS BY STATES

Most states require that any pet food sold within its borders be registered. Fees charged can be by company or by brand, and vary widely. Most must be renewed yearly, and some states also collect an inspection fee. State feed control officials that enforce pet food regulations are employees of the state department of agriculture and intended by AAFCO to be neutral parties without investment in the outcome of the process. They take samples of products in the retail market and submit them to an official lab for analysis to ascertain if the product meets the guarantee claimed on its packaging.

AAFCO wisely advises that a regulatory program's success is measured by the level of compliance, not the number of citations. Should a product test to be different than its guarantee – "out of spec" in industry jargon – different actions are suggested, depending on the inspector's viewpoint on matters such as inadvertent or deliberate, first time or frequent, large or small. If a first offense, and minor, the company may simply be sent a letter informing them of the findings. However, all inspectors have the authority to "red tag" a product and direct its removal from the market if they determine sufficient cause. It is counseled by AAFCO that violations be made known to the public and other industry members.

THE LABEL IN FACT AND THEORY

Suppose you find yourself having to explain to a Zulu tribesman the game of American baseball. You would start by saying the pitcher throws the ball so that the batter can hit it. This suffices for the tribesman to get the initial picture. But even a naïve baseball fan knows that the real aim of the pitcher is to throw the ball so the batter can't hit it.

This is somewhat analogous to pet food labels. The purpose and intent is to inform the consumer what is in the bag. However, to comply with the regulations in a candid and openhanded way can be tantamount to giving your formula to competitors, if they are knowledgeable. In the fiercely competitive world of pet food, industry executives are understandably reluctant to do this.

In reality, there can be occasional and subtle tricks of subterfuge at play. Gone, thankfully, are the days when many products listed as the predominant ingredient "grain and grain byproducts." This was a woeful ploy to satisfy the regulations without having to reveal anything. Grain and grain byproducts could be any of several dozen ingredients, but it was permitted and common. Use of this term was probably justified to the regulatory bodies as being definitive enough to comply with the spirit of the rule yet flexible enough to allow least-cost formulating, which the argument went, was in the best interest of the pet food buyer.

Least-cost formulating refers to computer formulating of the mix of ingredients to meet the nutritional specifications at the lowest cost possible. Computers are used because it is a formidable task to select from hundreds of ingredients, each with differing combinations of some 60 nutrients, and have the cost as low as possible. By using the term grain and grain byproducts, a manufacturer could buy whatever grain or byproduct costs the least, and change the formula accordingly without having to print new labels. To keep costs manageable, labels and bags are bought by the hundreds of thousands, and any change of label means a big inconvenience and expense in change of bags. No one changes labels capriciously, and any formula change is carefully coordinated with the exhaustion of on-hand bag inventory if at all possible.

Horse and farm animal feed bags often insert a tag in the top of the bag when it is sewn shut, which is a really useful approach as it lets one bag suffice regardless of label changes, and any outdated tags of this type sewn in the bag closure are simple and inexpensive to replace.

An example of the creative license that could be applied is eggs. Egg may be added to the formula as dry powdered eggs but is placed on the label as if it were whole eggs like people eat for breakfast. Whole egg is more expensive and an inconvenient ingredient to handle. Nutritionally, this is a harmless winking at the letter of the law that doesn't really fool a knowledgeable pet food nutritionist, but it does move the high quality egg ingredient quite a way up the list of ingredients (from say one to four percent), hopefully impressing some customers. Being difficult and expensive to identify in the laboratory, this inaccuracy is unlikely to be detected, especially given that feed inspectors have their hands full checking on basic claims like moisture and protein.

MELAMINE: HOW THE SYSTEM WORKS

In March of 2007 a major recall of cat food was reported by all the national and international news media. A toxic compound called melamine was soon identified. Rumor and speculation was that thousands of pets had died from contaminated food. Veterinary organizations reported 500 cases of renal failure and 100 deaths by the end of March. The actual number of deaths will never be known, but understandably there was widespread public outrage and calls for government regulations of the self-regulated pet food industry. The companies involved in the recall lost untold millions just in executing the recall, not to mention in sales. Ultimately, major companies recalled more than 5,000 different products. For affected pet owners, the loss of beloved pets, not to mention medical expense, was tragic.

There is an additional perspective important to consider. There is a system in place for these situations, and it worked. There can be no denying the heartbreak and sadness of this incident, but given the hundreds of millions of pet cats in the world, the carnage was small and quickly and efficiently contained, especially in light of the full story. The death of 100 cats could have been millions had it not been for industry safety procedures.

Pet food manufacturers print an indelible code on every package they make, identifying the product, date and time of production. With the company's name and address on the bag, anyone can contact the company and talk to an employee who can know exactly, by using the code on the package, the date, time of day and facility (plant) where the product was produced. From this, it is simple to know the product formula, and exactly what ingredients to investigate.

Additionally, many companies are routinely feeding their products to pets in ongoing market and food technology research, serving as an additional early warning. Such was the case in this recall, first volunteered by a company that noticed sickness in cats used for in-house taste preference testing. Within 30 days of the recall, veterinary diagnostic labs had tentatively identified the offending poison as melamine, an industrial chemical used in plastic manufacture. It was found in wheat gluten obtained from China. This was the same compound implicated in the even greater tragedy of deaths of infants in China fed adulterated baby formula.

When a feed is assayed for protein, melamine will cause an artificially high reading. If one is willing to completely forsake morals and ethics, adulterating a feed ingredient low in protein with melamine can be a means of circumventing routine quality assurance protocols in your own company as well as your customers.

The repercussions of this debacle were dramatic for China's feed ingredient business, but an invaluable lesson was learned, albeit in a horrendous manner.

REFERENCES

Academicians and professional nutritionists use as their authority... NRC. 2006. National Research Council. Nutrient requirements of dogs and cats. National Academies Press. 500 Fifth Street. Washington, D.C. 20001.

major companies recalled over 5000 different products... Weise, E, and J Schmidt. 2007. FDA limits Chinese food additive imports. USA Today. April 30.

13

WHAT TO FEED

The biggest question in most pet owners' minds is: What to feed? A normal concern to begin with, it becomes even more pressing with infinite options available, all claiming they have the best answer.

Human nutrition policy has increasingly second guessed itself in recent years, undermining public confidence in nutrition science. The earlier dictum that cholesterol is bad had to be modified. The advice to lower fat intake has not proven effective. Per capita consumption of fat has been declining for 30 years, but obesity has never been more prevalent. Margarine, the white knight saving us from the damage of butter, is now considered tantamount to a poison with its trans fatty acids, implicated in causing cancer. Meanwhile, butter has been praised anew for its high content of CLA (conjugated linoleic acid), shown to help prevent and even cure some cancers.

A pet owner's insight is further undermined by the fact that nutrition is rarely a crisis. This is nature's strategy for great adaptability as even bad nutrition by design at least gets us on to the next day. But wrong nutrition over time does bring on problems, and most people appreciate this. This is the source of their concern about what to feed their animals. What is the answer to the question; what is the best diet?

Everything discussed so far has been designed to bring us to this point. A review of the main points discussed in previous chapters can be summarized in what follows. For the record, in the Appendix (Tables 13, 14 and 15) you can find what the experts say in the way of recommendations for the cat, dog and horse. In all fairness, and despite all my sniping at policy makers, their tables are a sincere effort by well-intentioned scholars to summarize the current knowledge. They are a useful resource.

At the cellular level, there is far more in common across all species than not. There is a remarkable similarity in all creatures' biochemical metabolism. Each amino acid is the same precise molecular design everywhere in the world and serves the same function in every creature in the world, from a sea slug to an elephant. Another example is the enzyme system cytochrome C found in the mitochondria of all creatures everywhere in the world. The many hormones found in humans are essentially identical in form and function in all animals.

All creatures in the world use one of three basic feeding strategies: herbivore, carnivore or omnivore. A proper diet for one carnivore will adequately nourish any carnivore anywhere in the world. So too for a herbivore or omnivore. There is a surprising similarity in the nutrients all creatures require from their environment. For example, three hundred parts per billion (0.3 mg/kg) selenium in the diet dry matter is the average need of most animals, and it is the average content of the earth's crust. This is not a coincidence. It is simple logic.

Evolution adapted creatures to what was found on a consistent basis in the place where the biome was perfecting survival of the fittest. We do not find an isolated species that must have 200 parts per million of copper to survive, or one that is a unique exception in needing titanium at 10 parts per million. Everything seems to survive without any titanium.

For herbivores the world over, 10- to 12 percent dry matter protein is adequate for maintaining adults. This is because most plants encountered by foraging animals anywhere in the world have 10 to 12 percent protein in their dry matter. Younger plants can be higher in protein, and older plants lower, but most plants, while they are attractive to grazing animals, are just about the right level and kind of protein to support day to day sustenance for animals evolved to eat them.

Adaptability, more than any other single thing, allows species survival. Most all creatures have an exquisite ability to thrive on a range of different diets and to survive on a deficient diet -- for a time. This is because of the broad range of backup schemes perfected by evolution. It is because of this adaptability that we all survive, and also what fosters such confusion in everyone's mind about what is the best diet. Many diets seem to work, at least for a time, especially if when switching to a new diet it repairs a deficiency of the last diet. If you are feeding a diet deficient in protein and magnesium and you switch to a diet with adequate protein, there will be a partial improvement in pet health due to the increased protein, but the magnesium deficiency would still exist. A diet may actually appear to work wonders for a time, even though it too may be deficient.

Vegetarian versus meat. If people were true carnivores like the cat, a vegetarian diet would not work. Much of our experience is colored by the diets people eat. As everyone knows, there are people who seem to thrive quite well on a strict vegetarian diet, or a vegetarian based diet with some fish or egg or dairy products. There are also people who live to be 100 eating meat on a regular basis.

With all the hype of the modern media, it is easy to lose sight of the central concept illustrated by the wide range of diets that work. For omnivores, like dogs or people, a vegetarian diet can work and a diet devoid of vegetables can work. This is because it is possible to get everything you need, and nothing harmful, from either diet if it is properly selected.

What is lost in the typical debate about meat versus vegetables is what is not included in any good diet. When arriving at a healthful diet, be it vegetarian or meat based, the real key is the low level of total calories and especially the low amount of calories derived from starch and sugar.

The biggest error: Overfeeding energy in general and soluble carbohydrates specifically. The study sponsored by Purina (Kealy et al, 2002) and referenced in Chapter 3 should be adequate proof for everyone of what has been proven in numerous other species. Less calories lead to a longer life. Or, more correctly, excess calories shorten life and increase sickness. It is fine for puppies to be butterballs when nursing but do not be afraid to see a few ribs while they are maturing. Excess calories in the formative stages of life can predispose obesity in adults. Just as important, as we've discussed and as illustrated by the pictures of the emaciated Doberman in Chapter 4, even severe deficiency can be overcome with no permanent damage. If your puppy gets a little too thin for a couple of weeks, don't worry. Just feed him more. The thing to avoid at all cost is a puppy that is overweight the whole while it is growing to maturity.

Less work, more calories. Primordial mammals, and animals in the wild today, have to work hard each day for scant calories. Today, the work required to collect a day's worth of calories (for a pet or person) is one tenth of the effort expended by our ancestors and it can yield many times what is needed. Not only does nobody walk anywhere these days, we are consistently rewarding industry for inventing ways we can work even less (elevators, escalators, washing machines, juicers). In our cars, power seats and power windows have halved our daily work load, which can include a stop at a drive up window where we buy more calories in one meal than we need all day, and we never leave a sitting position. Our ancestors worked for hours to find as many calories as they hand out the window to you at a drive-through.

An adult coyote that hunted throughout a summer night to harvest one pack rat would expend maybe 500 calories, and consume about 220 calories, of which approximately eight percent would be from soluble carbohydrate[1]. From these numbers, it is evident the coyote had better harvest two pack rats. A house pet of identical size that lay around the house and yard all day, if fed according to the

---

[1] *250g per pack rat, live wt; X 80% water = 50g dry wt: X 80% digestible = 40g of nutrition. At ca.5.5 cal/g (ave of 70% protein and 30% fat), 40g = 220 cal.*

instructions on the typical bag of dog food, would consume over 1,000 calories, nearly half from soluble carbohydrate.

The illogic of too much dietary starch and sugar. The soluble carbohydrate found in any food in nature is lower than dry expended pet food. Certain parts of various plants at some times of the season or year can have soluble carbohydrate that approaches 20 percent. Drought may increase sugar, and the ratio of sugar to starch in a plant can vary depending if the draught came on suddenly or slowly (K.A. Watts 2009, referenced in Chapter 5). Some fruits and berries when fully ripe can be high in sugar on a dry matter basis, but as eaten, they are dilute with water. Honey is high in soluble carbohydrate. But these are the exception, and never part of the diet of an evolving mammal on a steady basis.

Our metabolism is designed to treat a spike in blood sugar as rare and valuable, and to save this energy bonanza in the body fat reserves. This is due almost exclusively to the action of insulin, the one hormone that lowers blood sugar and saves it as depot fat. The world that was the setting for mammalian evolution seldom offered any food that was high in sugar or starch, and on the occasion when it did, it was only for a short time. Quite simply, mammals are perfected to work hard for their nourishment in a world of little soluble carbohydrate. They are ill equipped to deal with a world where soluble carbohydrate is plentiful and exercise is absent.

The last big error: the gut micro flora is ignored. When the behavior of wild animals and feral pets is observed carefully, it is seen that food with bacterial loads of bewildering quantities is quite the norm. This is okay. Mammalian digestive systems are not only able to tolerate high amounts of ingested bacteria, but probably require it for optimization of the gut microflora. A canned pet food by definition, and by law, is sterile, but a sterile food is depriving the pet of needed microbial components intended by nature to be borne into the gut by the diet. Cooked pet foods short-change the gut microflora, and raw diets support it.

WHAT TO FEED

What is best to feed? When this entire book and the preceding summary are condensed still further, the first answer is: a mixture. A mixture of meats and meat scraps, vegetables and plant fiber sources, bones, organ meats, nuts, berries, some whole grains. A good vitamin mineral supplement does no harm and can be helpful. Some eggs are okay – they are nature's best protein . Present this mixture fresh and raw. There, finally, is the answer.

But please read on, as there are numerous variables, conditions and exceptions very much a part of any full answer to the question.

Raw versus cooked. There is not only nothing wrong with raw diets, they are probably better. There is no heating to destroy or alter protein, enzymes, vitamins or minerals. Digestibility for some nutrients is usually slightly higher in a raw food than if it is cooked. But raw food can be a source of bacteria, and in some cases harmful bacteria. If you are aware of basic microbiology and use proper handling of raw food, any concern is usually unfounded as the digestive system is quite capable of neutralizing the occasional pathogen.

But many people are not aware of the facts about bacteria. Food left out of the refrigerator or freezer will go bad in due time. If it is refrozen and thawed again, it will go bad even faster. Bacteria too have many survival tricks, one of which is to quickly ramp up reproductive spores if the temperature drops. Spores survive freezing, and blossom into bacteria upon thawing. Even without the stimulus of temperature change, a single bacteria cell can, if conditions are right, become a grossly visible colony in moist pet food left on the counter overnight.

Those in charge of food safety and regulation enforcement are mortified at the thought of raw pet food in the kitchen where people prepare and eat their own food. They see raw pet food as a vector for the introduction of pathogenic bacteria and the naïve pet owner as making things worse due to ignorance about microbiology. And sometimes they are right. For this reason, they much prefer that pet food be cooked. If a raw proponent, one needn't be overly preoccupied with the possible harm of cooking. It does diminish nutrition of some nutrients, such as denaturing certain natural enzymes and inactivating some vitamins, but it also greatly improves the shelf life of a product.

The issue is best described fairly as a tradeoff; raw has advantages and drawbacks, and cooked has advantages and drawbacks. A pet can be nourished properly with either. Raw is somewhat better, but you must understand microbiology. Cooked can be technically less nutrition (depending on how cooked and what ingredients are used), but it is much more convenient and lower in bacterial hazards than raw diets.

There is one situation where canned, meaning sterile, may be the preferred option. In dealing with a pet that is in poor health and especially lowered immune capability, a sterile food would introduce fewer bacteria of all sorts.

Probiotics and prebiotics. Probiotics are friendly bacteria such as found in yogurt. They are nearly impossible to add to an extruded or canned food as processing kills them. That is the main reason for processing in the first place, to kill bacteria and extend shelf life of the food.

Many pets live their life in an environment greatly diminished in bacteria, and this is not always good. If the number of bacterial cells in our intestines is ten times the number in our body (Chapter 5), would it not be logical to expect pets to also have numerous gut bacteria? Intestinal bacteria are crucial to normal life, so pets eating cooked food and living in a sanitized house may benefit from a quality probiotic. These must be added to the food as a top dress or fed to the pet as a salting on a treat they enjoy.

Most human health food stores and pet shops offer probiotics, with feeding guides. When evaluating a human probiotic to feed to your pet, adapt the feeding guide for humans to the weight of your pet. For example, if your pet weighs 60 lb, this is one half to one third of a person's weight. Feed your pet one third of a person's daily dose.

Prebiotics are not bacteria. They are nutrients or compounds that promote the growth of friendly bacteria and are covered in their own section (Chapter 7).

Vegetables and fruits. When considering the type or kind of vegetable to feed your dog, lean toward the ones high in fiber, a good example being celery. What you are trying to do is duplicate two sorts of plant material intake. The one type is what has been available for millions of years to a foraging omnivore: fresh grasses, tender shoots of young plants, and in season reproductive fruits such as squash or string beans. Fresh broccoli and cauliflower are good sources of nutrients like vitamin C and beta-carotene, and most all vegetables are low in soluble carbohydrate.

Potatoes, being high in starch, are of course an exception, and for this reason, I recommend keeping them to a minimum, both in frequency and amount. But there is no harm in an occasional potato.

The other type of plant material very common in an omnivore's diet is the intestinal contents of their prey. Carnivores particularly, and omnivores often, tend to eat other animals that are herbivores. When eating the intestinal contents of a prey animal, the predator benefits from the micronutrients so plentiful in a plant based diet, which includes many of the vitamins essential to all mammals and found in plants such as antioxidants and flavonoids.

Mammals breathe in oxygen and use it to chemically interact with nutrients to provide the fire of life. Plants do the reverse. They condense the carbons of carbon dioxide of the air into backbones of carbon (sugars are five or six carbons in a ring) and release oxygen. For plants, oxygen is a waste product. Evolution has perfected in plants many compounds to protect them from the damage of excess oxygen. These plant metabolites we refer to as antioxidants. When mammals eat plants, they consume these antioxidants, which protect them from oxygen damage, the same as plants.

Fruits as a class are widely consumed by omnivores for their nutrition. Blueberries, renowned for their antioxidant content, nourish everything from herbivorous deer and elk to omnivorous bears and coyotes. Coyotes and feral dogs will dine exclusively on fallen apples, and in so doing enjoy a treat virtually unknown to most modern humans, tree ripened fruit. Grocery store fruit is picked by design long before ripening as it is much more durable and withstands mechanical harvest, shipping and automated handling far better than ripe fruit. Ripe fruit must be eaten in a few days, not near enough time for modern market channels.

Along with the valuable nutrients in fruit, there can be appreciable amounts of sugar, so a diet of exclusively fruit could lead to excess soluble carbohydrate intake. However, much of the sugar in fruits is in the form of fructose, which does not require insulin to enter the cell. It is far less of a culprit in malnutrition than sucrose (which is half fructose and half glucose) or glucose. Furthermore, as fruits are high in moisture, modest amount of fresh fruit in the diet will add conservative amounts of dry matter to a complete diet, and only a portion of it as sugar.

Small, routine amounts of fresh fruits are not a problem for dog diets, with the apparent exception of grapes and raisins. According to the Animal Poison Control Center of the American Society for the Prevention of Cruelty to Animals, of 50 symptomatic dogs treated for grape or raisin toxicity in the year ending in April 2004, seven dogs died. The toxic dose of grapes is estimated to be .32 ounces for a 50 lb dog or 0.5 lb of raisins. The toxic substance is unknown, but 1/3 ounce is only a few grapes. One theory of the cause is mycotoxin, but this has not been proven.

Amount to feed. Most pet food labels provide a feeding guide and this is where to start in determining how much of a particular food to provide. In the absence of a printed feeding guide, feed adults two percent of body weight, in food dry matter, and growing pets 2.5 to three percent of their body weight in dry matter. Product labels must declare percent moisture. Dry matter is this number subtracted from 100.

Feeding guides are just that, guides. They are not intended, and there is no possible way, to correctly predict the right amount to feed for all individuals. Keep in mind that diet quality and therefore digestibility will influence feeding rate. Raw, frozen and freeze dried diets offer higher digestibility than cooked or grain based kibble. Always watch your pet closely and adjust the amount fed to maintain proper weight, regardless of what the feeding guide says. If your pet looks and acts the way you want, you're feeding the right amount.

Wet versus dry versus raw. Many people own a big dog or multiple big dogs, so dry dog food is much cheaper to feed than any other type of product. I have never said in this book not to feed dry dog food. Its drawback, that it contains too much soluble carbohydrate, I have discussed at length. To whatever extent dry dog food can be replaced by other food types, this soluble carbohydrate can be reduced. Canned pet food is typically lower in soluble carbohydrate, and as such is one product type to use in place of dry kibble. It too has its drawback. It is sterile.

Raw is the best diet type to use to reduce both the dry kibble and the canned products. As a pet owner's budget and life style permit, and as market availability allows, quality raw diets should be emphasized. The more this can be accomplished, the better will be your pet's nutrition.

Allergies. The underlying causes of some allergies include a definite component of heredity. By definition an allergy is a dysfunction or inappropriate response of the immune system, and traditionally best resolved by veterinary professionals. Allergies frequently go unresolved, or at best are managed into an acceptable level of existence for the pet. Sadly, even this is not achieved sometimes. One thing a pet owner can do, however, is to address their pet's diet.

A career-long friend of mine manufactured a pet food with the claim that if it did not cure a pet's skin condition, they would refund the customer's money. In their entire existence, they never refunded any money on this account. The distinguishing features of his diet were beef and beef organs, ground bone, low carbohydrate and freeze dried. I don't intend here to suggest such a diet as a cure for any allergy, but I do suggest that low soluble carbohydrate and raw are two concepts to consider.

In a determined search to explore any possible means of ameliorating a pet's allergy, don't overlook the gut. The gut is the site of much of the body's immune capability, and a raw, low soluble carbohydrate diet could help correct an imbalanced gut microflora that impinges on immunity. Reducing excess sugar and starch may not occur to a clinician. Hypoallergenic diets formulated around unconventional ingredient, if not also low in soluble carbohydrate, may have little effect.

Fish. Fish, especially cold water species, are good pet foods. Most dogs and all cats enjoy the taste of fish. The omega-3 content of fish is quite beneficial for the cat, with its lack of enzyme proficiency for fatty acid elongation.

Milk and dairy products of all kinds are good nutrition. Milk is the only thing found in nature that was made for the express purpose of being consumed as food. It is well designed for the purpose. Some adult pets lack the enzyme for digesting milk sugar (lactose) and too much milk may cause loose stools. For these individuals, some types of cheese may be a good option as cheese has the milk sugar removed.

Milk replacer. Most feed stores carry a line of products called milk replacers. These are fortified powdered milk intended to nourish orphaned or rejected newborns. For weanling puppies, milk replacer, reconstituted with warm water, is a tasty and nutritious supplement to add to a dry kibble. With use of the milk replacer in this way, it is also possible to buy a more economical dry kibble, due to the high nutrition of the milk replacer.

Enzymes. As a rule, it is not realistic to expect any enzyme to survive the intestinal milieu and cross the gut wall still retaining its functionality. Enzymes are proteins, often thousands of amino acids long. Many hormones, by comparison, are a few dozen amino acids. Assembled according to the exact dictates of DNA, enzymes literally run all of life in its infinite forms.

Biochemists speak of protein structure in terms of four levels. The first level is the sequence of amino acids, with each succeeding level a proscribed increase in complexity. One might think of the specific amino acids as bricks (first level) that form a wall (second level), the walls form a room (third level) that define a house (fourth level). Protein structure is very sensitive to its environment, and once disrupted, cannot easily be recovered. Frying an egg alters the protein and cannot be reversed, and shrunken wool is another example. It can never be un-shrunk. You can't un-fry an egg.

Enzymes in the gut have been fed into an elaborate and invincible machine designed expressly to break up proteins. That is what digestion does, it digests things. Insulin is a protein, a short chain of amino acids. If it could survive intestinal digestion intact and cross the gut wall still able to function, would millions of diabetics burden themselves with daily injections? However, ingested enzymes can be functional in the gut. After all, the body secretes many enzymes into the gut with instant effect: amylase, protease and lipase, to name three. However, it is not possible for an enzyme to cross the gut wall and still perform its original role in the body.

CONCLUSION

There are dogs and cats, exactly like our pets, that live in a wild state and nourish themselves very well. It is when people and domestication come into the picture that wrong nutrition becomes an issue. The most common way it is wrong is seen by the prevalence of obesity and the premature sickness obesity predisposes. There was never a problem easier to identify than obesity. However, even a cursory look into the problem reveals there are numerous paths to obesity, and its solution is far from simple. It is not a correct observation that calories in must balance calories out. Not all calories are equally fattening. Calories from starch and sugar are more fattening than an equal amount of calories from fat.

The fundamental concept at the base of all causes of obesity is that every species evolved in a constant struggle to find adequate food. There was no easily attained source of food, which meant that finding and procuring food involved a constant investment of energy. Further, there was no food that was abundant on a regular basis and very few foods available at any time particularly high in calories from soluble carbohydrate. This resulted in an equation only balanced by constant work yielding just enough calories. Sometimes it was barely enough, or enough for now, thanks to backup tricks for shortfalls.

Nature went to extraordinary lengths to find ways to enable survival of a species under this harsh economy of nourishment. There is a backup system immediately available in the face of almost any lack. Any food component, be it protein, fat, fiber (via hindgut fermentation) or carbohydrate, can be processed to energy, the most pressing need in the primordial world. There are, so far as we know, eight hormones that signal to increase blood glucose. Such redundancy abounds in cellular metabolism with just about every enzyme and messenger molecule so far discovered having been proved to serve multiple functions. These eight hormones would lead one to conclude that evolution put a high premium on keeping blood glucose supported and held up to a critical lower threshold.

There is only one hormone known to lower blood glucose: insulin. From this it could be deduced that nature did not find much reason to perfect a blood glucose lowering scheme. The one blood sugar lowering method throughout all life forms, insulin, is simplistic and without the backup and redundancy that is standard issue in all the rest of metabolism. Constant high blood glucose was not a problem encountered in the course of evolution.

All the backup and redundancy became the foundation of a remarkable adaptability, the indispensable key to surviving the frequent and sometimes prolonged periods of insufficient food. Nature never had to develop a system for dealing with constant excess. Nothing in nature ever offered an excess of any food for extended periods. Fruit ripened and died, fish and rabbits were elusive, plants went dormant, rain gave way to drought. Even if abundance was at hand, it was short lived and dilute in calories or nutrients. Most foods were high in moisture or fiber or both. Very few were high in sugar or starch. On the rare occasion when a food like honey or dates was chanced upon, and blood glucose spiked, insulin was yanked off the bench and thrown into the game. Cells were filled with glucose if needed, and the excess was saved as body fat.

The premise of this book is that mammals are exquisitely perfected to be able to survive in the face of intermittent and occasionally prolonged lack of food. Mammals are poorly adapted to deal with constant excess, particularly calories and especially calories from sugar and starch. Feeding a dry expanded food as the only source of nutrition to a dog, and definitely a cat, provides excess soluble carbohydrate, contributing to obesity and ill health. If concerned about your pet's health and nutrition, the first thing to do is to think about ways to decrease the feeding of starch and sugar.

END NOTES

From page 9, my exposure to business training...

I feel compelled to mention and add to the record just how accomplished Meyer Luskin was as a businessman. He and his wife recently donated $100 million to UCLA. Meyer accumulated this astonishing wherewithal entirely in his lifetime, starting out with no more advantage than any of us. One learned a lot if lucky enough to work for him.

from page 16, Basal Metabolic Rate...

This insight we owe to the genius of Dr. Samuel Brody, who showed us that BMR, in kilocalories per day, equals 70 times your weight in kilograms (pounds ÷ 2.2 = kg) raised to the ¾ power. This equation pertains to all warm blooded creatures. (Over the past few decades, this ¾ value, or .75, has been more closely calculated by scientists to be .73, but .75 is still used. Incidentally, body weight to the ¾ power can be accurately estimated by cubing the body weight then taking the square root twice. As most calculators have a square root button, it's not that hard to generate. Some human nutrition tables use this body weight to the ¾ power, or metabolic weight as it is sometimes called.) Brody's equation yields a tidy number but is rather useless in practical application. Once you awake and start going about your day, your energy needs go up, so the basal rate doesn't pertain.

Nutritionists do have equations for estimating energy needs (NRC 2006). Metabolizable energy (referred to as ME and explained in more detail in the next end note) for growing puppies is predicted by this equation:

$$ME \ (kcal) = 130 \ X \ BWa0.75 \ X \ 3.2 \ X \ [e(-0.87p) \ -0.1]$$

$$Where: p = BWa/BWm$$

$$BWa = actual \ body \ weight \ at \ time \ of \ evaluation \ (kg)$$

$$BWm = expected \ mature \ body \ weight \ (kg)$$

$$e = base \ of \ natural \ log \approx 2.718$$

While I applaud the application of proper science, the mere thought of trying to use this equation gives me facial tics. It may be comforting to know one can calculate exactly what growing puppies require in the way of energy, but in reality, pet food nutritionists don't use these equations very often. For comparison sake, the above equation predicts that 16-week-old Labrador puppies need 1,934 kcal of metabolizable energy.

from page 17, energy terms and definitions...

Thankfully, for the sake of clarity, there is some order to the interrelationship of energy categories. Gross energy is always more than digestible energy, which is always more than metabolizable energy. The total calories or gross energy of a food or diet can be determined in a precise scientific procedure using a device called a bomb calorimeter. An exact amount of the diet is placed in a vessel surrounded with water and it is completely burned. The heat given off with this complete burning is captured by the water, which rises in temperature. The rise in temperature is a direct function of the heat (calories) in the diet. A diet high in fat, which is a good source of calories, will yield a higher gross energy reading. Diets high in minerals (called ash) give a lower value, as minerals do not contribute calories. Gross energy readings from a bomb calorimeter are one method for comparing diets for energy. I did one once as a college student.

It turns out, you may be relieved to know, that bomb calorimeter readings on a diet are not very useful either. There are many reasons for this such as the fact that cellulose, which is poorly digested by monogastrics, yields the same heat increase of the water as sugar, which is very digestible. The gross energy value doesn't provide any clue as to how available the energy is to an animal. So nutritionists use a more applicable description of energy in a diet, called digestible energy. Digestible energy is the energy content of a diet that can be absorbed into the body. This is determined with accuracy only by feeding trials, also called digestibility trials, discussed elsewhere. The advantage of digestible energy over gross energy is that it corrects for things like fiber that add to the calories of gross energy but are not digested by monogastrics. The drawback to this energy descriptor is that while it measures what gets taken into the body, it ignores the fact that not all calories or nutrients that get into the body stay there to be used productively, or are used the same way. Calories from fat are treated differently than those from starch or sugar, a fact that has been ignored for the last 50 years.

Here is the place to discuss how to calculate a diet's energy, which means talking math for a moment. Just like the bomb calorimeter, you needn't worry about the day to day utility of this but a balanced review of the topic deserves this discussion. An estimate for determining a diet's digestible energy can be generated mathematically. While only an estimate, it can be useful for comparing one diet to another. To do this math, it is assumed, after metabolic processing, that protein and carbohydrate yield four calories per gram, and fat nine calories per gram. A diet has six components all adding up to 100 percent; moisture, protein, carbohydrate, fat, fiber and mineral. Minerals, fiber and moisture are treated as contributing zero calories, so all that is required is to allot four calories for each gram of protein and carbohydrate, and nine calories for each gram of fat. Moisture, protein and fat are listed as a percentage on all pet food containers. The problem is carbo-hydrate and minerals. They are not listed on any pet food container. But there is a way to back into these values. If the percentage of any five of the components is known, the six is known automatically by difference. If the percent moisture, protein, fat, fiber and mineral are all subtracted from 100 percent, the remainder is carbohydrate.

Assume a bag of dry food is 12 percent moisture, 21 percent protein, 10 percent fat and 4 percent fiber, as claimed on the label. Of the five we need to know, the one missing is mineral. This is rarely disclosed on a label, so we must guess. This is not as reckless as one might think. Mineral is invariably about 3 percent in a canned diet and 10 percent in a dry diet. Using an ash level of 10 percent for this dry diet, and subtracting it from 100 along with moisture (12 percent), protein (21 percent), fat (10 percent) and fiber (4 percent), leaves a carbohydrate value of 43 percent.

If given values as a percentage, you can automatically convert percentage to grams per 100 grams. In other words, 21 percent protein on the bag also means 21 grams of protein in 100 grams of dog food. With protein at four calories per gram, this particular food then has 4 X 21 = 84 calories from protein in every 100 grams. For fat, the math is 10 X 9 = 90 calories in 100 grams of the food, coming from fat. The carbohydrate, calculated by difference to be 43 percent adds 43 X 4 = 172 calories to every 100 grams of the food.

These three types of calorie sources add up to a total of 346 calories/100 grams of the food (84 + 90 + 172). This 346 calories is in 100 grams of food, as fed. This is converted to a kilogram basis by multiplying by 10. (It is converted to a pound basis by multiplying by 4.54.) All are converted to a 100 percent dry matter basis by dividing by 0.88 because the food is 88 percent dry matter (the reciprocal of 12 percent moisture, claimed on the label). Since 2016, AAFCO has mandated calorie content on all labels. This is useful for comparing one diet to another, but not much help in understanding nutrition.

Metabolizable energy is yet a further refinement of the energy description of a diet. It is the most useful description, being the least variable and most reliable way to com-pare one diet to another. The principle aspect of metabolizable energy is that it is the digestible energy of a diet (the calories taken into the body) corrected for loss that shows up in the urine, expelled gases and increase of body temperature--sometimes called the heat of digestion, things of no value for nourishment. These components, the result of metabolic processing, vary with the individual as well as diet makeup, and are a net loss to the animal. Metabolizable energy can only be determined exactly in a laboratory with repeat experiments using animals in metabolic chambers that save all feces, urine, shed hair, expelled gases and carefully control environmental conditions. Needless to say, few such trials are conducted on pet foods, and nutritionists resort instead to calculations and observation.

END NOTES

from page 22, digestibility trials...

I would like to illustrate the utility of a digestibility trial by relating research we did some years ago. I was working for a company that made a dry diet for bears in captivity. Some of their famous customers were Smokey the Bear, resident of the National Zoo in Washington, D.C., along with the first giant pandas to arrive from China. Smokey was found as a cub in the wake of a forest fire in New Mexico. The diet was fully balanced to the best of our knowledge to adequately nourish a mother bear with cubs. Reports were coming back from various zoo customers that polar bears on the diet had loose stools.

The diet was formulated to nourish an omnivore, which bears are, in that they will eat almost anything. I reasoned that perhaps the polar bear was more of a carnivore, and as such could not digest the carbohydrate component of the diet. Further, I hypothesized the lack of breakdown of the starches and sugars left these ingredients for bacteria to thrive on, and these bacteria produced a mild diarrhea and the loose stools we were hearing about.

We did a digestibility trial using two 400 pound polar bear cubs. This was quite an adventure. I ended up grateful that I did not work with primates, as the cubs proved quite my match in intellectual wattage.

It was necessary to drain the cubs' little swimming pools because bears sometimes defecate in the water. To do a digestibility trial, we needed to save all the feces. Without the pools, we had to fabricate drinking places for the bears, or basically retrofit a drinking fountain. They destroyed anything we tried including four-inch thick concrete troughs with iron rebar. What finally worked was welding together steel boxes and bolting them to the exhibit bars with engine head bolts. Normal bolts, even if half inch, were instantly snapped off by the cubs tugging on the welded steel water box. My first lesson: polar bear cubs (cubs mind you) have strength beyond our comprehension.

The cubs' exhibit was actually two with a dividing wall between them. This wall of bars had a sliding door, similar to a jail cell door, which was opened and closed by pulling a T-bar handle from outside the exhibit. This T-bar handle hung idle next to the exhibit when the door was closed. Both cubs were in one side of the exhibit with the door closed and I was in the other side gathering refused food and feces for our digestibility trial. Unknown to me, one of the cubs reached through the bars and lifted up the T-bar handle. Thus occupied and unable to do more, his buddy slid the door open and they both then headed into the side of the exhibit where I was studiously scooping up feces. Forthwith, I excused myself from their presence via the door at the back of the exhibit. As my heart rate headed back below 200, I watched in frustration as the cubs frolicked in the feces I had left behind (theirs, not mine). They had never shown the least interest in their feces until they saw me collecting it with diligence and care. My second lesson: polar bear cubs are smart. Real smart.

Our next countermove was to chain the T-bar handle to the exhibit bars so the cubs could not change at will from one side to the other. To accomplish this, I tempted the cubs to the back of the exhibit by baiting them with fresh fish. My associate in the opposite corner could then safely chain the T-bar handle to the exhibit bars. When my assistant proceeded to chain the T-bar handle, one of the cubs left me and the fish and darted over and smacked my assistant's hand with his paw, then speared a link of the chain with a claw and pulled it into the exhibit. Now in proud possession of the chain, the cub suddenly lost all interest in it.

As we watched bewildered, the cub pushed the chain back into the corner of the exhibit where my associate was waiting at the T-bar. Ignoring the chain, the cub then headed over to me to see if he could beg some more fish. When my colleague retrieved the chain to resume his task of chaining the T-bar, the cub instantly did an about face, leaped into the corner and pulled the chain back into the exhibit again. So the people had set out to dupe the cubs and in 90 seconds, the cubs had seen right through our scheme and countered with one of their own that we completely fell for. Third lesson: polar bears are capable of predictive reasoning, deception and malice of forethought. I was eternally grateful that I did not have to spend a moment in the same thousand square miles as a marauding adult polar bear.

We did finally manage to outwit the cubs and complete a trial. I must point out that this was in an earlier era, and zoo management today would not permit the procedures we employed. Exhibits today are better designed to allow bear movement without exposing people or bears to risk. But the polar bears had the last laugh. The trial results showed that polar bears are fully capable of digesting carbohydrate in a dry feed, at about 85 percent, the same as most any omnivore, so my hypothesis was invalid.

I presented this research at the national zoo meeting that year in Calgary. In attendance was Dr. Charles Jonkle, who had tracked and tagged more polar bears in the wild than anyone. When I asked him about normal polar bear stools in the wild, Dr. Jonkle replied that when feeding on ringed seal, their predominant prey nine months of the year, their feces looked like a square yard of green paint. So not only was my hypothesis misguided, but the entire premise for the research was misguided. Stools can be loose to begin with and still be normal.

However, a unique point was learned. On the occasion when the polar bear might encounter carbohydrate, such as a summer blueberry patch or raiding the town dump in Churchill, Canada, it was a fully functional omnivore. But in those days, the digestibility trial to prove this had not been done, and we added to the body of knowledge in this regard. I must admit, at the time, this insight seemed rather mundane compared to my new appreciation for polar bear intelligence.

from page 30, chitin in the world...

The abundance of chitin in the world, second only to cellulose, was told to me decades ago along with the observation that nothing could digest chitin. This struck me as illogical, lest we be up to our eyeballs in chitin with insects alone producing tons a day. I reflected on a bass fish swallowing a crayfish whole, yet excreting a soft paste, and reasoned chitin digestion (by an enzyme called chitinase) was more common than thought. We proceeded to demonstrate that the bacteria of a cow's rumen could digest chitin by feeding radioactive chitin and following the radioactivity. We obtained the radioactive chitin by feeding radioactive glucose to cockroaches who deposited this tagged glucose in the chitin of their shell. As they matured and outgrew their skin, we stole it from them when they shed it. You had to be attentive as the first thing a cockroach does on shedding its skin is eat it for recycling. All this was fun science in a day when radio tracer work was still prevalent. The real challenge as it turned out was inventing a chitin assay, which did not exist at that time.

from page 38, radio carbon dating...

Isotope ratio analysis is familiar to most as radiocarbon dating. There is an isotope of normal carbon that differs slightly in atomic structure. Archeologists have learned how to read and interpret the ratios of carbon 12 (normal, stable configuration, 12C) and carbon 14 (the non-stable radioactive configuration, 14C). There is a small but steady level of 14C in all carbon, the basis of the radiocarbon dating. The key is the property of non-stable. Slowly, over time, 14C spontaneously reverts to 12C. As an animal goes through life, and plants too for that matter, carbon cycles in and out of the body as intended by nature; but upon death, the carbon content obviously stops this fluxing and is chiseled in stone, so to speak. However, the trace amounts of carbon 14C in its bones, being non stable, continue to decay or revert to the lower, more stable forms of carbon 12. Because carbon 14 decays at a slow, constant and precise rate (called its half life), it is possible to assay for 14C, and given its amount relative to 12C, extrapolate back to the time when carbon flux stopped, the time of death, and hence an estimate of the time of life.

from page 58, Doberman...

The full story of the emaciated Doberman is worth telling. My wife is one of those people who talks to the newspaper, TV, iPad or cell phone as if they were logical knowing beings fully capable of common sense dialogue. One morning I was working in my office as she was reading the paper in the next room. "Oh, aah! These people ought to be shot! Who would do this?!" She was obviously outraged by something she was looking at in the paper and I was supposed to concur as if the same picture was right before me on my computer screen and I knew exactly what she was upset about.

What she was looking at was the picture shown in the text of the emaciated Doberman. He had just been rescued by animal control and taken to the shelter for first aid. The shelter management was so upset they called a reporter and Rojo, as he was dubbed, got full coverage, front page, above the fold.

My wife explained to me about the starving dog, impatient that I should now abandon saving all the other animals in the world and come be enraged with her about this one skinny dog. I absentmindedly tossed off to her that they'd better be careful and not give it too much protein or they'd kill it, like World War II allies liberating concentration camp survivors (killed by well-intentioned but tragically lethal steak and eggs). And they'd better not give it too much energy, or they'd kill it, like Karen Carpenter (the famous singer who, while recovering from anorexia, was overfed energy causing a heart attack.)

Pretty soon I hear a conversation she is having on the phone. Well, strictly speaking, I hear half of the conversation. "Yes, hello, I was reading about Rojo in the paper and my husband is an animal nutritionist, and he says you'd better be careful and not give him too much protein...yes. That's right. And he says you better be careful and not give him too much energy, or he'll die of a heart attack like Karen Carpenter...Yes. That's right... Oh...oh...well, yes...Ok...Yes. Okay."

The half conversation ends and soon a person (that'd be my wife) appears silently in my office. With a tone of voice guaranteed to strike horror in a husband's heart, she says, "Honey...?" I look at her, heart pounding. In the same sweet, terrifying tone she continues, "You know that Doberman pictured in the paper this morning?"

To get to the punch line, Rojo came to our house "just to recover" which he did in fine style for the next ten years. He proved the most delightful companion and recovered 100 percent except for one small mental scar. As he was curled at your feet while you watched TV if you went to stroke him with your bare foot he would dash into the next room or outside if he could get there. He never got over his fear of a foot off the ground near him. So I do concur with my wife, some people ought to be shot.

from page 62, hormones...

Another hormone of more recent discovery called leptin caused no small amount of excitement when first investigated, as it led to weight loss in diverse species. One means by which it did this was to enhance the feeling of satiety caused by food intake, thereby ending meals sooner. This initial enthusiasm soon faded when it was learned that obese individuals tended to show a marked insensitivity to leptin sending researchers back to the drawing board. A clear understanding of how satiety and hunger are signaled, from where (the liver, gut or brain) and exactly what are the messengers is far from clear. This is not for lack of study, as many researchers are pursuing this question, and the entire topic is actively debated.

from page 64, glycemic index...

To determine a food's glycemic index is not easy because it involves several human volunteers and multiple bleedings after they have ingested 50 grams of glucose, followed at a later time by an amount of test food that delivers the same amount of sugar. Each volunteer's rise in blood sugar, both in speed and duration, after eating the test food, is compared to their rise in blood sugar after eating glucose. Any published value hopefully represents the average of several different volunteers as there are always variations from one person to the next. Glucose is arbitrarily assigned a numerical value of 100, and all foods are ranked against this 100 value of glucose. Some foods, thought very few, actually have a glycemic index near 100, such as Thailand rice, which is at 98. Other rice cultivars are much lower.

from page 92, probiotics...

Suppose a company wanted to market a probiotic. The modern day identification and selection of a probiotic follows a routine and rigorous process, enabled by recent gains in the science, art and craft of molecular biology. It can take years and involves all the sophisticated analytical machines of the genome hunters.

As a hypothetical example, a group of dogs with a history of affliction with, say, twisted stomach is assembled, along with an identical group free of the affliction. Feces from each dog from each group are subjected to a process that identifies, via a DNA fingerprint, the microbes unique to each dog. With this information in hand, it is possible to compare the afflicted and healthy dogs and hopefully identify a common bacterium in either one group or the other. A bacterium common to all the healthy dogs would be one to select for, and a bacterium common to all the afflicted dogs would be one to select against.

Let's assume a bacterium was identified that was found almost exclusively in the healthy dogs. It is put through a further series of screens: It must be easily grown in large numbers, survive gastric pH, bile acids and intestinal enzymes. Derived from a mammalian GI tract, it should pass these tests. However, few bacteria will survive the high heat and humidity of manufacturing used for extrusion (dry kibble) and none will survive the canning process, which results in a sterile food. For extruded pet foods, this is sidestepped by dusting the probiotic on the outside of the food after extrusion. In most agricultural feeds, processing is not used, so route of addition is not an issue.

A candidate probiotic must next prove of benefit to the host animal. Benefit can take numerous forms such as greater weight gain, improved feed conversion, firmer stools, less flatulence or healthier skin and coat.

Results must be reproducible and pronounced enough to be seen or measured. In the case we are considering at the moment, the benefit would be no twisted stomachs. Animal owners are understandably reluctant to pay extra for a benefit they can't see or measure but if your German Shepherds suffered twisted stomachs, and upon feeding a probiotic *it never happened again, you would certainly be inclined to always feed the probiotic. A demonstrable benefit is the pet owner's only assurance they are getting what they pay for, and that a probiotic is useful.*

Pet food manufacturers rarely absorb a cost they can't pass on to the end consumer, or at least advertise and induce greater sales. Many products easily demonstrate benefits in a controlled laboratory setting with numerous test animals compared to control animals, but the advantage is not great enough to be evident in the real world and fades into the fog of biologic variation from one individual to the next.

from page 133, minerals...

When considering what mineral form to include in a formula, nutritionists factor in potency (also referred to as concentration or purity or percent of element), cost and bioavailability, usually in that order. To illustrate, magnesium sulfate is the more expensive form of the element. Magnesium as sulfate is 17 percent magnesium, and in the oxide form 58 percent. The sulfate form is considered more bioavailable but not enough to make up for the fact that the oxide form is three and a half times more concentrated. Also, three and a half times as much magnesium sulfate would be required to add the same amount of elemental magnesium to the diet if using magnesium oxide. So in this case, the call is easy. You don't use magnesium sulfate, despite its better digestibility. It costs more and must be used at three and a half times the level, needing more space in the formula.

Space in a formula can become a problem. The comparison of magnesium sulfate to magnesium oxide illustrates this point. If you wanted to have 0.2 percent magnesium added to a diet, it would require 1.17 percent of the formula as magnesium sulfate. If magnesium oxide was used, with its much higher concentration of magnesium, only 0.34 percent would be required. This is a difference of 0.84 percent, nearly 1 percent.

Innumerable times I have searched in vain for "room" to add one percent of something into a formula. So formulating, in addition to awareness of bioavailability, also requires consideration of cost and ingredient potency, or percent concentration. Computers are a big help in keeping track of all this as hundreds of different ingredient options are evaluated.

APPENDIX

Energy Calculation. *Method of energy calculation for a pet food, using the guarantee information written on the label.*

EXAMPLE 1, dry type diet: Written on the bag and or label:

Crude protein	21%
Crude fat	10%
Crude fiber	4%
Moisture	12%
Ash	10% *(rarely disclosed, so assumed estimated value)*

1) Determine the carbohydrate amount.

This number is not declared on the bag, but can be estimated closely as follows:

a. Assume an ash value of 10% for a dry type diet, 3% for canned. [Ash is the sum of all minerals in the diet.]

b. Subtract protein, fat, fiber, moisture and ash from 100. In the example, this equals 43, and represents the grams of carbohydrate in 100 grams of diet, as fed.

2) Determine the calories in 100 grams of diet.

Multiply the protein and carbohydrate by 4, and the fat by 9, and add together. (21 X 4) + (43 X 4) + (10 X 9) = 346. [Protein and carbohydrate have about 4 calories per gram and fat has 9.]

3) Multiply the value from 2) by 10

The number of calories in 100 grams of diet is 346, so in a kilogram (1000 grams) the value is 3460 calories. This number is the kcal in a kilogram of the food. Dividing this by 2.2 yields the kcal per pound, 1572.

4) Convert the as fed amount of calories to a dry matter basis.

Because moisture content can vary greatly, diets are always compared on a 100% dry matter basis. This is done by dividing the as fed amount of calories by the percent dry matter. [Percent dry matter is 100 minus the percent moisture on the label, which in the example is 12, so the dry matter is 88%.] 3460 ÷ .88 = 3931. Thus, the caloric density of the diet in the example above is 3931 kcal/lb of diet dry matter.

EXAMPLE 2, Canned type diet: Label claim crude protein 10%, crude fat 8%, crude fiber 3%, moisture 70%. Assume ash = 3%.Kcal/kg of dry matter = 4642 (2110 kcal/lb).

Table 1 *Comparison, based on bag claims, of four major dry kibble dog foods purchases in a supermarket.*[1]

Food	Purina	Purina	Iams	Pedigree
Descriptor	Complete and balanced	Total nutrition	100% complete and balanced	Adult complete
Crude protein, %	21	26	24	21
Fat, %	10	16	10	10
Fiber, %	4.5	3	5	4
Moisture, %	12	12	10	12
NFE[2]	43	34	42	44
Linoleic acid, %	1.5	1.4	-	1.4
Calcium, %	1	1	-	-
Phosphorus, %	0.8	0.8	-	-
Vit A, 1000IU/kg	10	13	-	-
Vitamin E, IU/kg	-	100	140	225
Weight of bag, lb	8.8	8.0	8.0	8.8
Cost per bag	$7.29	$10.99	$9.99	$7.49
Cost per pound	$.83	$1.37	$1.25	$.85
Kcal/lb dry matter[3]	1801	1987	1787	1812
Kcal/kg dry matter	3962	4371	3931	3986
Cost/kcal,	$.52	$.78	$.77	$.53

[1] *Products, from left. Purina Dog Chow; Purina One, Adult Lamb and Rice; Iams, Active Mature; Pedigree Adult Complete Nutrition.*

[2] *Nitrogen Free Extract, an estimate of soluble carbohydrate. NFE is calculated as 100- (protein + fat + fiber + ash + moisture). Ash is rarely disclosed on a label claim and typically is about 9% on an as fed basis in kibble foods. On a 100% dry matter basis, these diets are, respectively, 49.67, 38.87, 46.68 and 50.24% soluble carbohydrate, for an average of over 46%.*

[3] *For detailed discussion of energy calculations, see **Energy Calculation** in the Appendi, page 171.*

Table 9 *Expanded. Glycemic Index (GI), and Glycemic Load (GL) of different foods.*[1]

Food (number of studies)	GI	GL[2]
Glucose (11)	99	-
Fructose (6)	19	2
Low (GI 1 to 30)		
Hummus (chickpea dip)	6	0
Peanuts (3)	14	1
Acorns	16	1
Milk, whole (5)	27	3
Agave Nectar Cactus (type of honey)	11	1
Cashews	22	3
Soybeans (2)	18	1
Kidney Beans (8)	28	7
Medium (GI 30 to 60)		
Ice cream (Hi fat)	37	4
Tortilla	38	9
Honey (11)[3]	55	10
Spaghetti (70), foreign	44	21
Strawberries, fresh	40	1
Plum	39	3
Peach	42	5
Pear	38	4
Pineapple	59	7
Grapefruit	25	3
Grapes (2)	46	8
Food (number of studies)	GI	GL[2]
Orange (6)	42	5
Apples	38	6
Banana (10)	52	12
Sweet corn (2), USA	60	20
Oat Bran	55	3

Table 9 (continued)

Peas (3), boiled	48	3
Carrots (4)	47	3
Wheat bread (2)	53	11
Whole Grain Bread	51	7
Coca Cola (2)[4]	58	16
Wheat, cooked	41	14
High (GI 61 to 100)		
Rice Cake Crackers	78	17
Rice (13)	64	23
Rice, Thailand	98	31
Potato (4)	85	26
Sweet Potato	61	17
French Fries	75	22
Corn Chips (Nachos)	74	21
Popcorn	72	8
Jelly Beans	78	22
Tapioca	70	12
Green Pea Soup	66	27
Wheat, Durham, boiled 20 min	61	27
Corn Meal	69	9
Porridge (USA)	75	17
Rice Krispies (breakfast cereal)	82	22
Shredded wheat (breakfast cereal)	83	17
Corn Flakes (breakfast cereal)	81	21
Wonder Bread (USA)	70	10
Donut	76	17
Mars Bar (candy)	65	26

[1]Source: International Table of Glycemic Index and Glycemic Load Values 2002. Foster-Powell, K., S. Holt, and J. C. Brand-Miller. Am. J. Clin. Nutr. 2002; 765-756.

[2]*Glycemic Load can be influenced by several things, such as test serving size, or fiber. For example, oat bran and sweet corn are nearly identical in GI, but quite different in GL. This is most probably due to the fiber content of oat bran.*

[3]*Honey was listed with a wide range of GI, from 35 to 87. Pure honey is listed at 58. The*

high level of fructose (GI=19) in honey may be part of the reason its GI is low for a high sugar food.

[4]Coca Cola may also benefit from its high fructose content, which keeps its GI lower than expected. Many soft drinks are made using high fructose corn syrup, which is sweeter than sucrose (table sugar).

Table 13 Nutrient requirements of the growing and adult cat, and lactating queen. Percent in diet dry matter, or amount per kg of dry matter.[1] (mg/kg = ppm.) From Nutrient Requirements of Dogs and Cats. National Research Council, 2006. National Academies Press. Washington, DC 20001.

Nutrient	Adult	Growth	Lactation
Protein, %	20	22.5	30
Methionine, g	1.7	4.4	6
Taurine, g	.4	.4	.53
Fat, %	9	9	9
Linoleic acid, g	5.5	5.5	5.5
Arachidonic acid, g	.06	.2	.2
EPA + DHA, g[2]	.10	.10	.10
α-linolenic acid, g	0	.2	.2
Calcium, g	2.9	8	10.8
Phosphorus, g	2.6	7.2	7.6
Magnesium, g	.4	.4	.5
Potassium, g	5.2	4.0	5.2
Sodium, g	.68	1.4	2.6
Chloride, g	.96	.90	4.0
Iron, mg	80	80	80
Copper, mg	5.0	8.4	8.8
Zinc, mg	74	75	60
Nutrient	Adult	Growth	Lactation
Manganese, mg	4.8	4.8	7.2
Selenium, mg	.3	.3	.3
Iodine, mg	1.4	1.8	1.8
Vitamin A, IU	3330	3330	6660

Vitamin D, IU	280	224	280
Vitamin E, IU	38	38	31
Vitamin K (as menadione), mg	1	1	1
Thiamin, mg	5.6	5.5	6.3
Riboflavin, mg	4	4	4
Pyridoxine, mg	2.5	2.5	2.5
Niacin, mg	40	40	40
Pantothenic acid, mg	5.75	5.75	5.75
Cobalamin, µg	22.5	22.5	22.5
Folate, µg	750	750	750
Biotin, µg	75	75	75
Choline, mg	2550	2550	2550

[1] based on a diet that delivers 4000 kcal of metabolizable energy per kg of dry matter.

[2] Eicosapentaenoic acid + docosahexaenoic acid

Table 14 Nutrient requirements of growing and adult dog, and lactating bitch. Dry matter basis. Based on two authorities.

	NRC[1]			AAFCO[2]	
	Maint	Growth[3]	Gest/Lact	Maint	Repro
Protein, %	10[4]	22.5	20	18	22
Fat, %	5.5	8.5	8.5	5.5	8.5
Linoleic acid, g/kg	11	13	13	11	13
A-linoleic acid, g/kg	.44	.3	.8		.8
EPA + DHA[5], g/kg	.44	.5	.5		.5
Calcium, g/kg	4	12	8	5	12
Phosphorus, g/kg	3	10	5	4	10
	NRC[1]			AAFCO[2]	
	Maint	Growth[3]	Gest/Lact	Maint	Repro
Magnesium, g/kg	.6	.4	.6	.6	.6
Potassium, g/kg	4	4.4	3.6	6	6
Sodium, g/kg	.8	2.2	2.0	.8	3

Chloride, g/kg	1.2	2.9	3.0	1.2	4.5
Iron, mg/kg	30	88	70	40	88
Copper, mg/kg	6	11	12.4	7.3	12.4
Zinc, mg/kg	60	100	96	80	100
Manganese, mg/kg	4.8	5.6	7.2	5	7.2
Selenium, mg/kg	.35	.35	.35	0.35	0.35
Iodine, mg/kg	.88	.88	.88	1	1
Vitamin A, IU/kg	5050	5050	5050	5000	5000
Vitamin D, IU/kg	550	550	550	500	500
Vitamin E, IU/kg	30	30	30	50	50
Thiamin, mg/kg	2.25	2.25	2.25	2.25	2.25
Riboflavin, mg/kg	5.25	5.25	5.25	5.2	5.2
Pyridoxine, mg/kg	1.5	1.5	1.5	1.5	1.5
Niacin, mg/kg	17	17	17	13.6	13.6
Pantothenic acid, mg/kg	15	15	15	12	12
Cobalamin, mg/kg	.035	.035	.035	.022	.022
Folic acid, mg/kg	0.27	0.27	.027	.22	.22
Choline, mg/kg	1700	1700	1700	1200	1200

[1]*National Research Council, 2006. Based on a diet of 4000 kcal M.E./kg dry matter.*

[2] *Association of American Feed Control Officials. 2016. Based on a diet of 4000kcal M.E./kg dry matter.*

Both authorities assume intestinal synthesis of Vit K and biotin to meet needs.

[3]*Puppies, 4 to 14 weeks old.*

[4]*This value is significantly lower than AAFCO regulations, and is based on feeding high quality and highly digestible protein.*

[5] *Eicosapentaenoic acid + docosahexaenoic acid*

Table 15 Nutrient recommendations for horses, percent or amount in total ration, or amount per day, dry matter basis[1].

	Maint	Preg. mare	Male	Peak lact	4-6 months	Light Work	Moderate	Heavy*
Dry matter intake, % BW[2]	1.5-2.0	1.5-2.0	1.5-2.0	2.0-3.0	2.0-3.5	1.5-2.5	1.75-2.5	2.0-3.0
Protein, %	8	10	9.6	13.2	14	9.8	10.4	11.4
Calcium, %	0.24	0.44	0.29	0.52	0.60	0.30	0.31	0.35
Phosphorus, %	0.17	0.33	0.29	0.34	0.34	0.22	0.23	0.25
Magnesium, %	0.09	0.11	0.11	0.10	0.08	0.11	0.12	0.13
Potassium, %	0.30	0.36	0.36	0.42	0.30	0.37	0.38	0.39
Sodium, %	0.10	0.10	0.10	0.10	0.10	0.30	0.30	0.30
Sulfur, %	0.15	0.15	0.15	0.15	0.15	0.15	0.15	0.15
Vit A, IU/day, X1000	15	30	22.5	30	173	22.5	22.5	22.5
Vit D, IU/day, X1000	3.3	3.3	3.3	3.3	6.03	3.3	3.3	3.3
Vit E, IU/day	500	800	800	1000	8003	800	900	1000
Thiamin, mg/kg	3	3	3	3	3	5	5	5
Riboflavin, mg/kg	2	2	2	2	2	2	2	2

Research is lacking for authorities to recommend for other vitamins. Adequate gut microbe synthesis is assumed for healthy horses.

Trace minerals, all horses, mg/kg of feed dry matter: Iron 50, copper 10, cobalt 0.1, manganese 40, zinc 40,iodine 0.1, selenium 0.1.

*Light work is 6 hr/week of sweat producing work at 70°F (21°C); moderate, more than 9 hr; heavy, more than 15 hr.

[1]This table is a synthesis of the tables in the older NRC (1989) and the recent one (2007). The newer tables do not list percent, using instead, in the case of protein, grams required per day, with no mention of how much total feed is eaten.

It is footnoted that an assumed feed intake of 2% of body weight is used for certain mineral recommendations. Using this 2% figure for a 1100 lb (500 kg) horse at maintenance, a dry matter intake of 22 lb (10 kg) is predicted. The recommended protein for such a horse is 540 grams, which would be 5.4% of the ration as protein. This is a low figure. Not to dispute this—it does speak to horses' hardiness—simple grams are an awkward approach for most horse owners. This table therefore is presented using percent of diet for recommendations for protein and macro minerals.

[2]There are formulas for predicting a horse's energy requirements. A 500 kg horse at maintenance needs 15.2 to 18.2 Mcal of digestible energy per day (NRC 2007, p9). Because energy needs are so variable (see Chapter 2) the horse owner is advised to rely on observation of body condition.

[3]Daily Vitamin A, D and E needs increase linearly from 4 to 24 months of age, as a function of body size. Recommended diet potency, IU/lb dry matter, for growing horse: Vitamin A, 909; Vitamin D, 363: Vitamin E, 36.3.

RUINED BY EXCESS PERFECTED BY LACK

Table 7. *Composition, in grams/100g, of prehistoric foods, as found and eaten in the wild. Calcium and phosphorus in mg/100g.*

Food	Water	Protein	Fat	Ash	Total Carb	Fiber
Leaves						
Spinach	91.40	2.86	0.39	1.72	3.63	2.2
Lettuce	95.07	1.36	0.15	0.62	2.79	1.3
Brussels sprouts	86.01	3.38	0.30	1.37	8.95	3.8
Tender shoots						
Celery	95.40	0.69	0.17	0.75	2.97	1.6
Asparagus	93.20	2.20	0.12	0.58	3.88	2.1
Broccoli	89.30	2.82	0.37	0.87	6.64	2.6
Nuts						
Almonds	5.25	21.26	50.6	3.11	19.74	11.8
English walnut	4.07	15.23	65.21	1.78	13.71	6.7
Pine nut	2.28	13.70	68.4	2.59	13.08	3.7
Acorn	27.9	6.15	23.86	1.35	40.75	
Cashew	5.20	18.22	43.85	2.54	30.19	3.3
Europe chestnut	48.65	2.42	2.26	1.13	45.54	8.1
Macadamian	1.36	7.91	75.77	1.14	13.82	8.6
Pecan	3.52	9.17	72.0	1.49	13.86	9.6
Hazelnut	5.31	14.95	60.75	2.29	16.7	9.7
Seeds						
Flax	6.96	18.30	42.16	3.72	28.9	27.3
Squash/pumpkin	6.92	24.50	45.85	4.88	17.81	3.9
Safflower	5.62	16.18	38.4	5.47	34.29	
Sesame	4.69	17.73	49.67	4.45	23.45	11.8
Sunflower	1.20	19.33	49.8	5.6	24.07	11.1
Berries						
Grape	81.30	0.63	0.35	0.57	17.15	0.9
Strawberry	80.6	0.58	0.60	0.80	17.36	5.4
Blackberry	83.20	0.71	0.50	0.30	15.30	1.50
Tubers						
Peanut	6.50	25.8	49.2	2.33	16.13	8.5
Carrot	88.29	0.93	0.24	0.97	9.58	2.8
Sweet potato	77.28	1.57	0.05	0.99	20.12	3.0
Russet potato	78.58	2.14	0.08	1.13	18.07	1.3

All Sugars	Sucrose	Glucose	Fructose	Starch	Calcium	Phos	USDA #
0.42	0.07	0.11	0.15	0	99	49	
0.78	0	0.36	0.43	0	36	29	
2.20	0.46	0.81	0.93	0	42	69	
1.83	0.11	0.55	0.51	0	40	24	
1.88	0.23	0.65	1.00	0	24	52	
1.70	0.10	0.49	0.68	0	47	66	
4.80	4.54	0.12		0.73	248	474	
2.61	2.43	0.08	0.09	0.06	98	346	
3.59	3.45	0.07	0.07	1.43	16	575	
							12058
5.91	5.81	0.05	0.05	23.49	37	593	12087
					27	93	12097
4.57	4.43	0.07	0.07	1.50	85	188	12131
3.97	3.9			0.46	70	277	12142
4.34	4.2	0.07	0.07	0.48	114	290	12120
1.55	1.15	0.41			255	642	
1.00					43	1174	12014
					78	644	12021
0.30					975	629	12023
2.73					70	1155	12037
16.25					14	191	9131
					21	27	
					15	13	
3.97					92	376	
4.74	3.59	0.59	0.55	1.43	33	35	
4.18	2.52	0.96	0.70	12.65	30	47	
0.62	0.13	0.25	0.23	15.86			11353

Table 7. (Con't). Composition, in grams/100g, of prehistoric foods, as found and eaten in the wild. Calcium and phosphorus in mg/100g.

Food	Water	Protein	Fat	Ash	Total Carb	Fiber
Fruit						
Peach	88.87	0.91	0.25	0.43	9.54	1.5
Apple	85.56	0.26	0.17	0.19	13.81	2.4
Pear	83.70	0.38	0.12	0.33	15.46	3.1
Tangerine	85.17	0.81	0.31	0.38	13.34	1.8
Cherry	91.4	0.40	0.30	0.21	7.69	1.1
Other						
Mushroom	92.4	3.09	0.34	0.85	3.28	1.0
Squash	44.6	1.21	0.18	0.62	3.35	1.1
Avacado (meat)	72.3	1.96	15.41	1.66	8.64	6.8
Date						
Fig						
Vertebrates						
Venison	71.15	21.8	7.13	0.88	<1.0	0
Rabbit	74.51	21.79	2.32	1.12	0.71	0
Frog	81.9	16.4	0.31	1.4	0.71	0
Quail	71.67	22.6	2.99	1.27	0.71	0
Chicken	75.8	19.56	3.91	0.96	<1.0	0
Quail egg	74.35	13.05	11.09	1.1	0.41	0
Trout	71.87	20.5	3.46	1.31	<1.0	0
Catfish	80.36	16.4	2.82	0.96	<1.0	0
Invertebrates						
Clam	81.82	12.3	0.97	1.87	2.57	0
Mussel	80.58	11.9	2.24	1.59	3.69	0
Snail	79.2	16.1	1.40	1.30	2	0
Termite	10	36	44	1.5	1	8
Silkworm		23	14			
Locust		75	20			
Honey	17.1	0.30	0	0.2	82.4	0.21

All Sugars	Sucrose	Glucose	Fructose	Starch	Calcium	Phos	USDA #
8.39	4.76	1.95	1.53	0	6	20	9236
10.39	2.07	2.43	5.9	0.05	6	11	9003
9.8	0.78	2.76	6.23	0	9	11	9252
10.58	6.05	2.13	2.4	0	37	20	9218
					12	11	9001
1.65	0	1.48	0.17	0	3	86	
2.2	0.03	0.75	0.95	0	15	38	
0.3	0.08	0.10	0.11	0.11	13	54	9038
					11	201	17343
					12	226	17180
					18	147	80200
					10	228	5159
					25	168	5096
0.41					64	226	1140
					67	271	15115
					14	209	15010
					46	169	15157
					26	197	15164
					10	272	90560
82.14	0.89	35.7	40.94	0	6	4	19296

Symbols

A

B

C

Dear reader: The nature of this book requires some terms appear frequently. At the risk of complicating a word search, but rather than hinder a determined student it was elected to cite each rather than delete any incident of a word's use.